The Fat Revolution
Cookbook

INDULGENT FULL-FAT RECIPES—
WITHOUT THE SUGAR OR THE GUILT

PURPLE
LOTUS
PUBLISHING

DISCLAIMER

All the information contained within this publication is of the nature of general comment only, and is not in any way recommended as individual advice. The intent is to offer a variety of information to provide a wider range of choices now and in the future, recognising that we all have widely diverse circumstances and viewpoints. Should any reader choose to make use of the information contained herein, this is their decision, and the author and publishers do not assume any responsibilities whatsoever under any conditions or circumstances. It is recommended that the reader obtain their own independent advice.

National Library of Australia Cataloguing-in-Publication entry:
Cronau, Christine.

The Fat Revolution Cookbook: Indulgent full fat recipes—Without the sugar or the guilt
3rd ed.
Rev. ed of: Great Health is a Piece of Cake. 2010.
Includes index.

ISBN 9780980878707 (pbk.)
1. Low carb, high fat (LCHF) 2. Nutrition. 3. Cooking (Natural foods)
641.5637

Published by Purple Lotus Publishing
Moggill, Qld, 4070
Email: purplelotuspublishing@iinet.net.au

BOOK COVER

Styling by Tash Kimlin [facebook.com/whimsypetitestyling]
Photography by Rose Hewartson [rosehewartson.com]
Cover design by Ryan Jackson [designgururyan.com]

BOOK LAYOUT

Food styling by Jaime Reyes [jaimereyes.com.au]
Food photography by Cathy Taylor [cathytaylorphotographer.com]
Book layout design and typesetting by Stacey Grainger [ruby-door.com]

Printed and bound by McPhersons Printing [www.mcphersonsprinting.com.au]

What people are saying about *The Fat Revolution Cookbook*

"Finally a cook book with simple messages on real healthy eating that is not only going to keep you well, full of vitality, looking great and assist with weight loss but also open your eyes to how we really should be fuelling our bodies and why. Christine's simple range of healthy meals, desserts and snacks and her informative easy-to-read and understand information is a great start for anyone wanting to turn their eating around and start living a cleaner healthier life. I am so excited to have some great logical information at hand and from this I can build my own recipes and create my ideal healthy body." **Dominique Rizzo**, Celebrity Chef and Educator "Pure Food Cooking"

"As a Naturopath, I have recommended many healthy eating books to clients over the years but this is one book you can trust to provide healthy and delicious recipes that everyone in the family will love and benefit from as well." **Kim Balson N.D.** *(Hons), Naturopath, Hormone Consultant, Author Woman to Woman: Managing Your Hormones Safely and Naturally*

"Christine's sumptuous recipes will nurture your body and tantalise your taste buds." **Dr Sarah J Buckley M.D.**, *Author Gentle Birth, Gentle Mothering: A Doctor's Guide to Natural Childbirth and Gentle Early Parenting Choices*

"This book is a wonderful summary of many dietary truths that are often misunderstood by the average person. Written in an easy to read format, it introduces these concepts in such a way that even the most modest beginner can understand. Recognising the great pleasure that food is to most people, Christine offers healthy alternatives to your favourite foods, without the hidden nasties. With recipes that are quick to make and contain simple, nutritious ingredients this is definitely a book to have on hand." **Sandi Cooper** *N.D. BHSc Nat. ATMS, Naturopath, Nutritionist*

"A visual feast of wholesome recipes, accompanied by inspiring quotes and logical research that has stood the test of time. Nature holds the wisdom of health." **Julie Phillips** *B.A.R.M, Dip Shiatsu & Oriental Medicine, Cert. Whole Food Medicine, Kinesiology, Dynamic Healing, Training Cert IV, et al*

"Any book about food that is inviting, educational and fun to use has my approval — Christine has done fantastic work in her careful preparation. Australia leads the way in the western world for obesity epidemic. Eating for pleasure rather than sustenance has become a primary tool in producing morbid obesity. A recent study in a prestigious medical journal explained a clear connection between visceral fat (the dense fat found surrounding intra-abdominal organs) not only is unsightly but also is dangerous to our health. The study revealed this type of fat is linked to the development of metabolic syndrome, to cardiovascular disease and to premature death.* I congratulate Christine on her work in promoting a better and tasty way to eat while improving healthy outcomes at the same time." **Dr. Graham Lyttle** *DO. DC. MSc., FIMCA. MANPA.*

"I was given this book as I was beginning a strict eating plan for myself, so I've found it very valuable. This book pulls no punches and covers all the important stuff. The meals are appetizing & inspired with easy to follow directions; who would've thought sugar-free desserts could be so delicious! Reading this book is a great way to kick start good eating habits – for the whole family, and I'll be encouraging my kids to use these recipes too." **Kristen Morrison**, *Author Naturally Better and Cofounder of The Grow Foundation, for Naturally Better Kids*

"Christine has created a cookbook that demonstrates you can cook a nutritious meal quickly & simply, with very little preparation, using minimal ingredients. This is great news for all the busy people who believe they 'don't have time to cook'. Congratulations Christine for producing an easy read, common sense book that shares the benefits of eating 'real' food." **Deborah Wray**, *Founder of Wray Organic (chain of organic grocery stores)*

"I simply love it!" **Sandy Grant**, *Owner Wray Organic Indooroopilly*

"Christine is the epitome of health and wellness! Not only does she practice what she preaches, she always offers advice and support to anyone else wanting to eat healthier and live better. This book has great information about what "real" food is, and how processed food is affecting our health. I love being able to make healthy food for my family and the dessert/sweets recipes for special occasions. I would recommend this book to anyone with kids to show them that you can make healthy food that is quick and easy, and that kids will eat!" **Jo Atkinson**, *Mother of 3*

"I have been raving about this cook book to everyone, every chance I get! Finally a cookbook with easy, full flavoured recipes that are sugar-free, authentically nutritious and nourishing for the soul; that my kids love!!!! This cookbook not only provided me with much wanted recipes, it also fed my need to learn. Christine's depth of knowledge and wisdom about food is extensive. A very user friendly, wise, and delicious addition to everyone's kitchen." **Carolyn Summers**, *Mother of 2*

"I loved this cookbook! It's wonderful to find such a straightforward sensible guide to healthy eating. The recipes I've tried so far are easy and taste great and the advice is easy to understand. A great investment for a busy family." **Rachel Patterson**, *Mother of 3*

"Christine's dedication to creating beautiful, simple, healthy meals is inspiring and refreshing. The recipes in this cookbook care for our family, in that the recipes are not just different ingredients thrown in together, instead the recipes are thoughtful and delicious in their combination of foods that nourish the whole body. I know that when I cook from Christine's cookbook, the whole family will be delighted by the different textures, gorgeous natural flavours and amazing taste! The ice-cream cake has become our new 'family birthday cake', even for our middle-of-winter birthday, it is just so delicious!" **Kelly Makin**, *Mother of 2*

"Christine has come up with a system that if followed, will enhance one's life on many levels. The benefits will be experienced physically, mentally, emotionally and even spiritually. Spiritually in that your sensitivities will not be deadened by poor eating habits, and thus your conscious connection will be strengthened to your more subtle (spiritual) layers of self." **Melinda Adams**, *Psychic Medium, Spiritual Healer*

*Pischon, T. et al. (2008). General and Abdominal Adiposity and Risk of Death in Europe. New England Journal of Medicine 359 (20): 2105-2120.

Dedication

I dedicate this book to my wonderful family. We have been, and continue to be, on an amazing journey together.

To my daughter Anna, who lights up my life with her beautiful energy. You are so precious, and I am so grateful to have you in my life.

To my son Zac, who is the most amazing teenager I know. You are wise beyond your years, and have such a beautiful, gentle soul.

To my husband Randall, who has been instrumental in taking our family in a positive direction. There would be no book without you. Thank you for all your support. You rock my world, and I am so privileged to be sharing my life with you.

CONTENTS

INTRODUCTION

Diet and fat: The biggest health blunder in history!

Why a fat revolution? The low-fat craze was supposed to make us thin; it was also supposed to prevent heart disease, stroke, and many other modern diseases. The result? It did the opposite.

In Western countries, over half of the population is overweight or obese (in my early 20s, I was one of the many constantly battling with my weight). And, if something doesn't change, those numbers will increase to 80 or 90 per cent. And, modern chronic disease like heart disease, diabetes, Alzheimer's, auto-immune diseases, cancers, and so much more are out of control. Statistics show that, generally, we have been following recommended health guidelines. So, why aren't they working?

Research shows that conventional health guidelines are based on out-of-date information that was never correct. And, most of the damage comes from the idea that saturated fat is bad for us—bad for our weight and for our heart. I know this may seem shocking; the idea that saturated fat is the cause of heart disease is well and truly ingrained in modern society.

However, the concept that saturated fat is unhealthy is actually very new; it was first suggested in the 1950s. Prior to that, humans have been enjoying saturated fat (guilt free) for millions of years. Around two and a half million to be more precise. And, we enjoyed our saturated fat without suffering from heart disease, diabetes, and modern chronic disease in general. These diseases are actually very new; hence, the name 'modern.'

Sceptics love to say that when we were hunter gatherers, and eating all that saturated fat, we didn't live very long; and certainly not long enough to develop heart disease! But, actually, that is not the case. Research shows that if we survived the natural elements, we lived a very long time—and that we were free of modern chronic disease.

Eating healthy, high-quality food is one of the easiest and most powerful ways to create health on a daily basis.

DR CHRISTIANE NORTHRUP, WOMEN'S BODIES, WOMEN'S WISDOM

Studies of primal tribes show that they were tall, robust, and healthy, with straight teeth and wide, beautiful faces. So, when did we start developing these new diseases, and why? The very first documented case of a heart attack was 1926, but it was still fairly uncommon at that time. By the 1950s, heart disease was extremely common, and had experts scrambling for a solution.

So, what changed in the early 1900s? Did we suddenly start eating more saturated fat? No, we actually started eating less. Margarine and shortening had been invented and were becoming more popular because they were so cheap.

Between 1890 and 1920, sugar consumption doubled. Why? We started mass producing the sweet stuff for the first time. The very first confectionary companies were in business, and we developed a sweet tooth. And, we started replacing natural saturated fats with processed vegetable oils, which I call fake fats.

Then, in the 1950s, came the cholesterol campaign. Saturated fat was identified as the villain behind heart disease, even though there was no such evidence suggesting so. This idea was backed by the new big businesses profiting from replacing these saturated fats, and governments were lobbied to change their dietary recommendations. At the time, the decision was highly debated. The McGovern committee was formed to end the debate. Scientists could see there was no evidence to back the claims that saturated fat was unhealthy, but their pleas fell on deaf ears; Senator George McGovern said, "I would only argue that senators don't have the luxury that a research scientist does of waiting until every last shred of evidence is in." Thus, the low-fat era began.

The vilification of fat also created a new problem. We had to replace fat with something—fat is where the flavour is. When they took the fat out, they replaced it with sugar. And, because we were no longer eating fatty foods like butter, cheese, eggs, and cream, we had to replace those with something too, and that something was carbohydrates.

Our diet changed radically in the last 100 years, and so has our weight and our health. And, as our weight became a problem, we came up with new ideas to solve the problem. One of these was the calories in, calories out theory.

But this theory is full of holes; actually, it doesn't work at all. The first problem is that different calories act differently in the body. Some calories prompt our body to store fat and some don't. Interestingly, the higher calorie foods such as saturated fat are the least likely to prompt our body to store fat. And, the lower calorie foods, such as low-fat grain and diet products are the most likely to prompt our body to store fat. This is why the Masai tribes in Kenya only eat meat, milk, and blood, a very high fat diet, and stay lean. And, why the Inuit, who consumed around 80% of their calories as fat, were trim and healthy. How could this be?

It goes against everything we know, right?

There is a very good reason why, and actually, it is based on very basic biochemistry. Biochemistry is studied by every health professional, but there is a small fact that is often conveniently forgotten.

Excess carbohydrates make us fat. Actually, back in the 1940s, the idea that fat might cause us to be fat was very new. A group of farmers heard about it and decided to try and fatten their pigs with saturated fat prior to market. To their surprise, the pigs lost weight and became more active! Even though saturated fat has twice the calories of carbohydrate, it acts completely differently in the body.

Why do excess carbohydrates make us fat? Carbohydrates, including sugars, are broken down into glucose, which can be used by the body or stored. But, we can only use or store a small amount at any one time. In fact, we can only store around 500g of glycogen in our muscle fibres and liver cells. After that, if there is excess, in most cases, insulin transports it to the adipose (fatty) tissue for storage. Is this a bad process? Absolutely not, and in fact, it was crucial in times of famine. When we had extra food, we stored more fat, which helped us through hard times. But, this becomes a problem if we eat mostly carbohydrates like we do today.

Because of the sheer amount of insulin being produced, and the sheer amount of fat being stored, the body gets tired of this very unnatural process and eventually stops making insulin; our cells also become insulin resistant. The result is type 2 diabetes. Then, we have surplus glucose, but no way to get it to our cells. And, interestingly, what happens when we can't get glucose to our brain cells? If that is the only fuel our brain is relying on, which it is on a high carbohydrate diet, then the brain cells start to die,

Refined sugar is lethal when ingested by humans because it provides only that which nutritionists describe as empty or naked calories. In addition, sugar is worse than nothing because it drains and leeches the body of precious vitamins and minerals through the demands its digestion, detoxification, and elimination make upon one's entire system. So essential is balance to our bodies that we have many ways to protect against the sudden shock of a heavy intake of sugar. Minerals, such as sodium, potassium, and magnesium (from vegetables) and calcium (from the bones) are mobilised and used in chemical transmutation; neutralising acids are produced, which attempt to return the acid-alkaline balance factor of the blood to a more normal state. Sugar taken every day produces a continuously overacid condition, and more and more minerals are required from deep in the body in the attempt to rectify the imbalance. Finally, in order to protect the blood, so much calcium is taken from the bones and teeth that decay and general weakening begin.

WILLIAM DUFTY, SUGARBLUES

and then we have dementia or Alzheimer's. And, rates of dementia are currently sky-rocketing; rates are expected to almost double in the next few decades. Why can't experts explain why this is happening? And, how will our health care systems handle the influx?

Not only do different calories act differently in the body, fats also make us feel full. They produce a hormone call Cholecystokinin (CCK). So, what happens when we take away the fats? We are hungry! Suddenly, our meals don't last very long, and we have to constantly eat, which is how we ended up with the widely-accepted idea that we should eat small, frequent meals. Carbohydrates are fast burning and we have to refuel often. Fats provide long-lasting energy, so when we eat fat, we actually eat less!

We need fats!

Instead of low-fat diets helping us lose weight, they made us gain weight. But, the damaging effects of low-fat diets go far beyond weight gain. The cholesterol campaign made us forget that fat and cholesterol are actually essential for:

- Good cell function (the cell membrane is made up of around 50 per cent saturated fat). Good cell function is the basis for good health.
- Energy, not surprising since energy is produced in the cells.
- Healthy skin (without fats, we can't keep our cell membrane strong, cells dehydrate, which causes wrinkles).
- Good brain function and development.
- Pregnancy and breastfeeding.
- Healthy development of children.
- Healthy organ function.
- A healthy heart (ironically).
- Sex hormones.
- Thyroid function.
- Healthy metabolism.

And, so much more! Fats contain essential nutrients. No wonder it has become common place to feel tired, moody, grumpy, and depressed with a low sex drive. Especially in women. Why? Because most of us have spent years dieting. We have severely compromised our thyroid, our hormones, our metabolism and more.

Primal societies prized saturated fats, and held them especially sacred for pregnant and nursing mothers and growing children. For example, the author of Child of Tibet says, "Tibetans love butter and think it is the cure for everything." Now, we have done a u-turn and told people to stay away from these fats at all cost. How tragic. If only the general public knew just what this was doing to their health.

There is a reason the Tibetans think butter is a cure for everything. It is full of powerful nutrients. Just one example is vitamin K_2. Grass-fed butter is full of vitamin K_2, and this all-important nutrient has now been virtually eliminated from our diet! The only good sources are grass-fed butter, egg yolk, and soft cheeses like gouda and brie. Does it matter if we are missing K_2? Absolutely!

Vitamin K_2 prevents heart disease. It prevents calcification in the arteries. And, if calcification is present as a result of a sugary diet, it helps reverse it. Ironically, the very foods we are warned about protect us from heart disease. As we learn more and more about this, it makes complete sense why we now have such an epidemic of heart disease. Research shows the true culprits behind heart disease are sugar and vegetable oils. And, we have taken away the fats that, ironically, protect us from heart disease.

Why else do we need K_2? Deficiencies lead to crowded teeth and tooth decay, bone weakness, reproductive issues, kidney stones, learning difficulties, fatigue, and in severe cases, seizures.

In addition, we need K_2 for brain health. K_2 is essential to produce sulfatides; lipids (fats) that are a must for good cognitive function. In fact, studies show that those with early stages of Alzheimer's have over 90% less sulfatides than others.

Vitamin K_2 is also essential for good digestion, blood sugar regulation, sperm production, and many other vital bodily functions. And, vitamin K_2 is only one of the nutrients we are now deficient in as a result of our low-fat phobia. For full details, The Fat Revolution has the whole story.

Many cultures have held saturated fats sacred for centuries—they understood how vital and nutritious they were. In Western countries, we have done the opposite and often go to every length possible to remove these treasured fats from our food. We make egg white omelettes and throw away one of the most nutrient-dense and health-promoting foods on the planet!

Clearly something is very wrong, even though many Americans [and Australians] have been conscientious about following orthodox dietary advice. They take exercise seriously, many have stopped smoking, consumption of fresh vegetables has increased, many have reduced their intake of salt, and a good portion has cut back on red meats and animal fats. But none of these measures has made a dent in the ever-increasing toll of degenerative disease [or weight issues]. We buy foods labelled as lowfat, no cholesterol, reduced sodium, thinking they are good for us. Why, then, are we so sick?... Politically Correct Nutrition singles out foods grown by independent producers—eggs and beef—but spares the powerful and highly profitable grain cartels, vegetable oil producers and the food processing industry; it sacrifices old-fashioned butter on the altar of the latest nutritional fad but spares pasteurized milk products and processed cheese; it gives lip service to the overwhelming evidence implicating sugar as a major cause of our degenerative diseases but spares the soft drink industry; and it raises not a murmur against refined flour, hydrogenated vegetable oils and foods adulterated with harmful preservatives, flavourings and colouring agents...

The diet dictocrats are strangely silent about the ever increasing trend toward food processing and the devitalisation of America's rich agricultural bounty. Food processing is the largest manufacturing industry in the country and hence the most powerful. This industry naturally uses its financial clout to influence the slant of university research and the dictates that come from government agencies. A 1980 study showed that almost half the leading officials at the FDA had previously worked for organisations the agency is mandated to regulate. The universities have equally powerful ties to the food processing industry.

A good example is Harvard University where [a doctor], head of the nutrition department for many years, began his career with several articles delineating nutritional deficiencies caused by white flour and a study on Irish brothers that positively correlated a high intake of vegetable oils—not animal fats—with heart disease. Soon after he became department head, however, the university received several important grants from the food processing industry. [The doctor's] articles and weekly newspaper columns then began assuring the public that there was nothing wrong with white bread, sugar and highly processed foods. He recommended one cup of corn oil per day to prevent heart disease, and in one article he even suggested Coca-Cola as a snack!

Most "Nutritional" cookbooks follow the politically correct guidelines, including all those approved by the American Heart Association. A good example is [a bestselling nutrition cookbook]. A brief introduction rehashing a few politically correct studies, said to implicate saturated fats as the cause of heart disease, is followed by pages of recipes loaded with sugar and white flour. The authors assure us the best thing we can do for our hearts is to replace butter with margarine and eliminate eggs and red meat from our diet, in spite of the fact that most studies, honestly evaluated, show that such a diet is not only useless but also harmful.

**SALLY FALLON,
NOURISHING TRADITIONS**

What's the answer?

Low carb, high fat (LCHF) nutrition represents a diet much more suitable for our evolution as humans; one lower in carbohydrates and higher in natural fats such as butter and coconut oil. LCHF provides the nutrients we need to thrive, without the excess carbohydrates that make us sick—and fat.

The full definition is actually low carb, moderate protein, and high fat. Eating more fat naturally keeps protein levels at a moderate level, which is the healthiest. If we overeat protein, then excess amino acids can be converted to glucose in the liver and the protein can start acting like carbohydrate. However, this is much less likely to occur when eating adequate fats. In addition, it is important to note that protein is essential; many times people hear that excess protein can act like carbohydrate, so they reduce it to a level far too low, which creates a whole host of other problems, including depression.

And, what about carbohydrates? For most people, eating a small to moderate amount of carbohydrates is healthy and normal. The problem arrives when we overdo them. Like I mentioned previously, we can only store or use a very small amount of glucose at any one time. When we consume more than that, we store fat, cause acidity in the body, and this leads to chronic modern disease. But, what exactly is LCHF?

What is LCHF?

Some people get a bit of a surprise when they see delectable cakes, chocolates, cookies and other culinary delights in this book...and think, that is not LCHF is it? The grain and sugar has been taken out, but buckwheat, potato, sweet potato, almond meal, raw honey and other ingredients are all carbs? Right?

Let me clarify. There are many versions of LCHF, ranging from very low carb (around 20 or 30 g per day) to general low carb (around 60 to 100 g per day, depending on your size).

Let food be thy medicine.
HIPPOCRATES

If you have heard that meat, cheese, and eggs are acid forming, you are not alone. It is a common myth, but completely untrue. Are these animal proteins acids? Of course. They are full of amino acids and fatty acids, which are necessary for good health, which is why many are called essential amino acids and essential fatty acids. But, they do not make our body acid, and in fact alkalise the body. Balancing pH is simple with a LCHF diet with the addition of your daily lemon drink (detailed later). To find out more, I wrote a small book on the subject called *Regulating pH—The Real Story*, which is available here: *christinecronau.com/ ph.*

If we are insulin resistant, and unfortunately most people are after being on a typical Western diet for a significant length of time, then 'healthy' carbs spike our glucose and insulin levels much more than they do in a healthy person. What does this mean? For many people, it is advantageous to drop their carbs much lower to start with to force the body back into its natural fat-burning state.

Most of us have heard that our natural preference for energy is glucose, or sugar, but this is completely untrue. We only become sugar burners as an emergency response. The problem is, if the sugar keeps coming in, we have to keep burning it, and then we become permanent sugar burners.

If we follow a very low carb diet for long enough, and remain in that fat burning state for long enough, then when most people reintroduce reasonable amounts of healthy carbs like I mentioned above, even potato, they remain in that fat-burning state. For many people, three months is enough to transition into a permanent fat burning state. Because I was extremely unwell when I started LCHF, and had a lot to heal, I initially stayed on a very low carbohydrate (under 20 g per day) diet for 12 months. But the great news is that when I returned to my ideal carbohydrate intake, which is under 60 g per day, I remained in that fat burning state, and have been burning fat for energy for over 14 years—even though I eat some potato, fruit, and other foods considered 'high carb.' Just as an example, if I eat a typical LCHF diet, such as:

- Lamb chops and eggs (and butter of course)
- Chicken thigh and vegetables (with more butter)
- Quiche and salad (and, you guessed it, more butter)

and then add:

- Strawberries and cream
- Banana muffin (with loads of butter)
- Potato chips fried in coconut oil

...which I am unlikely to do all in the same day, but just to prove a point, I am still under 60 g of carbs for the day.

If the damage is less severe, then simply going straight to a general LCHF diet will also put us in a fat-burning state. For example, children switch back to fat burning very easily. They are younger, have had less years of damage, and heal very easily. Men also tend go back to their fat burning state easily because they generally haven't spent years dieting like many women have.

Some people, especially women, have hormone imbalance, thyroid imbalance, and metabolic imbalance, most of which comes from a lifetime of dieting—and these often prevent weight loss, even on LCHF. Very low carb diets help heal these imbalances, and after a period of time spent healing, for most people, weight loss will naturally start to occur. Patience may be required here though. If we think about how many years of damage have been done, it can take a good while to recover.

Some people prefer to remain very low carb until they reach their goal weight, and generally, the weight loss will be much faster if they do.

How do you know how much carbohydrate, protein, and fat is right for you? Everyone has individual requirements based on their size. Members of my website can calculate their ideal carbohydrate, protein, and fat intake. This is absolutely not necessary; I didn't have exact ratios when I started LCHF, but it is an extra tool that can help. And, I can guarantee that most people will be shocked at just how much fat they can eat. For more information, refer to *christinecronau.com/member*.

For most people, LCHF means freedom. It means an end to diets, deprivation, eternal hunger, calorie counting, watching how much we eat, and all the other miseries that come with years of starving ourselves.

My story

Many people take one look at me and automatically assume that I am one of those lucky people who can eat whatever they want and never gain weight. In fact, if I had a dollar for every time I heard someone say, "She has a good metabolism, it won't work for you," I would have another income stream. But that couldn't be further from the truth.

My siblings and I grew up extremely poor, so my diet was almost exclusively carbohydrates. And, like most poor children, I grew up quite skinny and malnourished.

If we eat too many carbohydrates or not enough protein, our body becomes imbalanced. Sugar cravings are a symptom, just like a headache, and are a sign of imbalance in your sugar metabolism. They're a sign of a breakdown in communication between the systems responsible for maintaining the equilibrium of your sugar metabolism. Almost every person who enters my office is struggling with some aspect of insulin sensitivity and sugar imbalance. That means one or all of the three organs that are partners in the process—the liver, pancreas, and adrenal glands—are very likely in crisis.

**DR DARREN WEISSMAN,
THE POWER OF INFINITE
LOVE AND GRATITUDE**

I was recently at a gym, which was having a celebration, and they had an array of foods out on a table. It was covered with whole grain bread, some sort of polyunsaturated spread, jam and fruit juice. Every single item on that table would have been considered 'healthy' and conducive to weight loss, but instead, every last one of them was contributing to weight gain!

But, once I turned 18, I started stacking on the kilos. This is extremely common, which is why it is not uncommon to see photos of obese women in third-world countries holding scrawny, malnourished babies.

And, what about my genetics? Maybe they play a part? Unfortunately, I didn't have any help there either. My grandmother on my father's side was diabetic, and struggled with obesity her entire life. In fact, we only have one photo of her because she refused to have her picture taken; she was so embarrassed about her weight. The one photo we do have of her was taken after she embarked on an extreme diet prescribed by her doctor. She fasted for three days (no food at all), and then ate only 600 calories per day. She did this for a few years, and eventually got her weight down to her lowest, which was 82 kilos. She was extremely proud of herself, but of course, she was starving, and it was unsustainable. So, she put the weight back on, plus interest. She was over 150 kilos when she died.

The interesting thing to note is that she only ever consumed diet or low-fat food. Whenever we visited her, there was never a single box or container in the house that did not say "low fat" or "diet." Of course now I know that this was part of the problem, because low-fat products make us fat— they replace the fat with sugar or carbohydrate.

What about my Grandmother on my mother's side? She never became overweight, but only because she refused to. I remember one of her favourite sayings was, "No thank you, I need to watch my girlish figure." At the time I thought it was quite cute. It wasn't until later I realised how sad it was. She spent her entire life dieting and watching her weight. Eventually she had a stroke. And, unfortunately, this is not an uncommon side effect of extreme dieting. Saturated fats are essential for brain health. And, of course, after her stroke, she could no longer move, so she ate even less.

And, my own mother? Dear thing; she followed in her mother's footsteps and spent many of her earlier years dieting. She was always slim growing up, but I remember her grapefruit diets and the fact that she always left her yolks on her plate! She even tried the same diet my grandmother used, because it "worked." Sure, it worked, but only while she was on the diet!

Unfortunately, a lifetime of dieting takes its toll. She ended up with thyroid dysfunction, a damaged metabolism, and many other issues. She ballooned to over 90 kilos. She absolutely hates the way she looks, and like many women, describes herself as a "fat pig."

And, because her metabolism, hormones, and thyroid function have all taken such a beating over the years, she is now to the point that she does not even respond to a healthy low carb, high fat diet. Fortunately, she does respond to an extremely low carbohydrate diet, but it is now a lot harder for her to lose weight because of the damage to her body.

In answer to the burning question, I do not have a great metabolism or good genetics. Actually, I know for a fact, that based on my metabolism and genetic history, if I hadn't changed my diet when I did, I would now be extremely overweight, and probably obese.

I am not a naturally slim person who can eat whatever I want. In fact, I am quite the opposite. Once I started stacking on the kilos in my late teens, I was quite shocked and embarrassed about my weight. I of course tried all kinds of diets and they all failed miserably. I thought it was just my willpower. But, I have learned since then, it was nothing to do with willpower.

I eventually became a low-fat vegetarian, and became "super" healthy. I was extremely careful to combine foods so that I received "adequate" protein. I ate a lot of lentils and other pulses with brown rice and vegetables. My morning breakfast was whole-grain cereal with soy milk and a banana. My snacks were whole-grain rye bread with either avocado or nut butter. I followed conventional health guidelines and practically eliminated butter. According to conventional wisdom, it was the perfect diet. I was able to shed the weight, but instead of my health improving, it declined rapidly, and I was eventually diagnosed with chronic fatigue.

I was fortunate enough to be directed to the right place. The nutritionist I went to see was more educated than most and pointed me in the right direction. He informed me that it was my "healthy" diet that was doing the damage. Even though I was combining foods, my blood tests showed that I was severely protein deficient. I was losing calcium from my teeth and bones, and I was in my

> The doctor of the future will give no medicines but will interest his patients in the care of the human frame, in diet, and the causes of disease.
>
> **THOMAS EDISON**

late 20s. This is extremely common on high carbohydrate diets because too much sugar imbalances our pH and in a desperate attempt to regulate our pH, our bodies use phosphate from our bones and teeth. The phosphate is bound to calcium, which means we lose calcium from our bones and teeth.

I then changed my diet radically to low carb, high fat (LCHF). I started eating eggs and meat, and plenty of butter. I felt immediate benefit from eating fats again, but it had taken years for my body to get into that state, and it took me a good few years to fully recover. However, most conventional doctors, even if they recognise chronic fatigue as a disorder, think there is no cure. I am extremely grateful that I changed to this lifestyle at a fairly young age, and I have saved myself a lifetime of chronic disease and illness, because that is exactly where I was headed.

And, just a quick note to address my weight loss on my low-fat diet. Yes, I did lose weight. Why? Those "healthy" whole grains damaged my digestive system, and I started suffering from malabsorption. And, this is extremely common, which is why there are people out there who can eat bucket loads of sugar and are still thin. They may be thin, but if we don't absorb enough nutrients, we get sick. And, like most other people with leaky gut, I then started developing food allergies.

The great news is that now I indulge in the many things I used to think were off limits. Butter, cream, eggs, crispy bacon with all the fat, lamb chops (with all the fat), roast pork with crunchy crackling, duck and chicken with crispy skin. And, I never have to think about how much I eat, I never count calories, and I never, ever diet—and I love to eat! I have been my current weight for over 13 years and my health has never been better.

For the full story on how we got things so wrong, including the science that well and truly debunks the cholesterol myth, read *The Fat Revolution*. Like Professor Mann, previously a professor in Medicine and Biochemistry, said, "the diet-heart idea is the greatest scientific deception of our times." He was absolutely right.

The good news is that we now have full permission to indulge in full-fat cuisine—without any of the guilt. And, it is priceless!

LCHF in practice

Like I mentioned previously, there are many variations of LCHF; but here are some general guidelines.

The following meal plan is a rough example. Every person will have different carbohydrate, protein, and fat intakes depending on their size and how much exercise they do or don't do. And, carbohydrates can be lowered initially to fix hormone imbalance, insulin resistance, and other health issues, and to encourage the body into a fat-burning state. In this case, eliminate fruit, potato and carbohydrates such as muffins for three months or so (longer if you like).

> Life is too short to eat crap.
>
> JAMIE OLIVER

	Breakfast	Lunch	Dinner
Monday	3 poached eggs with hollandaise Plenty of butter	Chicken salad Banana muffin with butter	Sweet potato slice
Tuesday	3 fried eggs with bacon Plenty of butter Yoghurt	Roast vegetable salad with bacon Fruit salad with whipped cream	Stir fry with egg noodles
Wednesday	3 fried eggs with a lamb chop You guessed it, lots of butter	Spanish quiche with salad Berry smoothie	Buckwheat crepe with chicken and salad filling
Thursday	Devilled eggs with nitrate free ham Brie cheese	Crumbed chicken with vegetables Strawberry and banana cream iceblocks	Pea and ham soup
Friday	3 fried eggs with zucchini and sweet potato fritter Butter	Pork roast with crackling Vegetables Yoghurt with berries	Pumpkin soup with sour cream Boiled egg
Saturday	Spanish omelette Butter	Chicken pie Passionfruit cheesecake with whipped cream	Irish stew
Sunday	Scrambled egg with onion, tomato, and gouda cheese Butter	Egg salad with grapefruit Chocolate ice cream	Chicken soup

Note: A very early dinner is best for weight loss, digestion, and the body's nightly detoxification process. Bigger meals are best in the morning and lunch, with a lighter meal in the early evening.

Following a LCHF lifestyle means no more hunger between meals. And, our digestive system needs a break. It is much healthier to eat three meals a day, rather than continuous snacking.

And, add butter when you think you can. You probably don't get the impression from the above meal plan, but we add butter to just about everything. Our family of four goes through around two kilos every week. It does take time to get used to the sheer amount of fat you can eat, and it may take time for your body to adjust because it won't be used to the quantity, so take things one step at a time.

Foods to avoid

Unfortunately, most items in the supermarket are not real food, and need to be avoided. Some supermarkets are expanding their product ranges and may include selections of organic free-range meat, organic cold-pressed olive oil, the odd packet of organic sultanas, and other foods. But, stay away from the aisles and aisles of boxes and packages in the middle of the grocery store. Generally, the items to avoid are:

- **Sugar**—including corn syrup.
- **Low-fat and homogenised dairy**—it is full of additives and we need the fat!
- **Vegetable oils**—Canola and other vegetable oils, margarine, vegetable shortening, and fat substitutes; these are new, processed oils are extremely damaging to the body.
- **Processed grains**—white rice, white flour, boxed cereals, granola and muesli, commercial breads (even the ones advertised as whole grain; they are full of sugar, soy protein isolate, and preservatives. The grain also hasn't been prepared adequately for easy digestion).
- **Soy**—a modern, processed food that causes health issues. For more information, read *westonaprice.org/soy-alert*. The only healthy soy products are fermented products like miso, tempeh, natto and tamari (wheat-free soy-sauce).

- **Fake meat**—this is not real food. It is usually based on soy and full of artificial ingredients. It is normally sold in the health food sections of the supermarket and in health food stores, so people assume it is healthy.
- **Soft drink / flavoured soda**—most of these are just sugar and chemicals.
- **Commercial fruit juices**—most are made with reconstituted juice, which is similar to sugar syrup. Many also have sugar and additives. They also contain a lot of fructose, which is just as damaging as sugar in large amounts.
- **Commercial honey**—it has been pasteurised and has lost all its enzymes and nutritional value.
- **Food additives**—including sugar substitutes.
- **Commercial salt**—the nutrition has been removed and aluminium is used as an anti-caking agent.
- **Commercial baking powder**—it is full of chemicals. Healthy options are available at health food stores.

The easiest way to avoid the items listed is to stop buying packets. I buy the occasional packet or bottle from the organic grocery store (after carefully reading the label to see if it is unprocessed, and has no sugar or other additives). Yes, even the health food store can sell items that are unhealthy, so checking the list of ingredients is essential if it has been pre-prepared.

Foods to include

Now, for the good news. Here is a list of real food that is healthy and delicious:

- **Grass-fed meat**—free-range, pasture-fed (if it is organic, it will be free-range).
- **Organic eggs**—the only way to truly guarantee free range or pastured is to buy organic, unless you know the farmer!
- **Quality fruit and vegetables**—organic is best where possible. Use fruits and vegetables that are in season, and try to get as much variety as possible (including colour).

Make a commitment to keep your body free of toxins, both physical and emotional. Don't contaminate your body with dead food or drink, toxic chemicals, toxic relationships, or toxic emotions in the form of anger, fear, or guilt.

DEEPAK CHOPRA

My personal nutrition approach is simple. If it grows, eat it. If it doesn't grow, don't eat it.

LOUISE HAY, YOU CAN HEAL YOUR LIFE

Many cultures have held saturated fats sacred for centuries—they understood how vital and nutritious they were. In Western countries, we have done the opposite and often go to every length possible to remove these treasured fats from our food. I once had a fascinating conversation with a Tibetan monk. I heard that Tibetans think butter is the cure for everything, so I asked him about it. He said, "Oh, yes, yes!" He then said, "We put it in our tea!" He went on to explain all the other uses. He also said that Tibetans only cook with butter or animal fat, not with oils. He said, "Oils smell. Tibetans don't like smell." We could learn a lot by going back to the old traditions, and understanding that saturated fats are vital for a long and healthy life.

- **Grass-fed butter and cream**—try to get quality, grass-fed butter and cream, as unprocessed as possible. We get beautiful cream from small local dairies, which is sold at the local fruit shop. And the difference is amazing; the cream is much thicker and richer than the cream available in most supermarkets.

- **Grass-fed yoghurt, cheese, and milk**—commercial yoghurt is made with milk solids (milk powder), which contains oxidised cholesterol; the only type of cholesterol that is damaging. Purchase quality organic yoghurts if you can. They also have not been homogenised. Stick to the softer cheeses such as gouda, edam, feta, brie, camembert, havarti; the hard yellow cheeses in the supermarket have not been traditionally cultured. Always buy unhomogenised milk.

- **Cold-pressed oils**—extra-virgin coconut oil is my favourite oil and has a high smoking point. I prefer to use the saturated fats like butter and coconut oil the most (full of short and medium chained fatty acids). Extra-virgin olive oil is lovely to use occasionally on salads or mayonnaise.

- **Quality condiments**—unrefined salt (pink Himalayan or rock salt), apple-cider vinegar, and tamari (naturally fermented soy sauce that is wheat-free).

- **Quality sweeteners**—raw honey and stevia (a very sweet plant that is hundreds of times sweeter than sugar). Stevia has no fructose and does not spike blood sugar. Raw honey has been getting a bad rap because it is around 40 percent fructose, but it is a nutritious sweetener, full of antioxidants, minerals, enzymes, and vitamins. Some of the nutrients in raw honey reduce its glucose response. Agave syrup is loaded with fructose, and isn't a healthy option. Dextrose has become a popular sweetener because it doesn't have the fructose, but it is highly processed, and any highly processed sugar will spike blood sugar levels, so I prefer stevia and small amounts of raw honey.

- **Filtered water**—invest in a reverse-osmosis water filter to remove the chemicals from your water. This is the only type that will remove fluoride from fluoridated water.

Tips for maximising health

For maximum health benefits:

- **Balance pH**—Unfortunately, most people are over-acid after consuming a western style diet. What this means is that we have too much acid waste, and our body is unable to eliminate it. As a result, we get less oxygen to our cells, our metabolism changes, we become a breeding ground for yeast and fungus, and we literally start to degenerate. Acid stress is generally the underlying cause of all degenerative disease—and also causes weight gain. pH imbalance is one of the biggest factors that can prevent weight loss because we start storing acid waste in our fat cells to protect our organs.

  If you have heard that meat, cheese, and eggs are acid forming, you are not alone. It is a common myth, but completely untrue. Are these animal proteins acids? Of course. They are full of amino acids and fatty acids, which are necessary for good health, which is why many are called essential amino acids and essential fatty acids. But, they do not make our body acid, and in fact alkalise the body. Balancing pH is simple with a LCHF diet and the addition of your daily lemon drink (detailed later). To find out more, I wrote a small book on the subject called *Regulating pH—The Real Story*, which is available here: *christinecronau.com/ph*.

- **Take a daily lemon drink on rising**—Lemon juice, lime juice, and apple cider vinegar all alkalise the body and are great digestive aids. Make a daily lemon drink with all three in a glass of filtered water. Most people are too acid, especially after eating a regular, mainstream diet, so this is a must, both for weight loss and health. In the winter, pour a little boiling water in your drink to warm it up (before you add the juice and vinegar). You can also add a squeeze of lemon or lime to your drinking water throughout the day. Drink with a straw to protect your teeth.

- **Chew your food thoroughly**—To digest food adequately, it needs to be chewed approximately 35 times per mouthful; longer if it is meat. This sounds difficult but actually makes food more enjoyable and will help with weight loss.

pH imbalance causes acidic waste to be stored in fat cells, which causes weight gain. Dr Lynda Frassetto, researcher and professor of Medicine and Nephrology at the University of California San Fransisco, found that because of the sheer amount of acid waste our bodies are forced to deal with, they end up stockpiling it in our adipose (fatty) tissue. We do this to protect our vital organs from degradation and failure. Our fat is literally saving our organs.

> Happiness for me is largely a matter of digestion.
>
> LIN YUTANG

> All happiness depends on a leisurely breakfast.
>
> JOHN GUNTHER

- **Drink away from meals**—Drinking with meals is a habit for many, but it dilutes digestive enzymes, making food harder to digest. Ideally, stop drinking half an hour before your meal, and start drinking again an hour after your meal.

- **Include cultured food in your diet**—Humans originated in a world without refrigeration, so our bodies were designed to ingest the good bacteria that formed when foods were cultured and fermented, which is what our ancestors did to preserve food. To keep your gut healthy, it is important to eat cultured food two or three times a day. There are plenty of cultured foods that you can include in your diet, but a lot of them can be overwhelming to make. The cultured foods easiest to incorporate are yoghurt, soft cheeses, apple cider vinegar, raw cultured butter (if you have access to it), tamari (wheat-free fermented soy sauce), and kombucha (a fermented drink becoming more and more common in organic grocery stores). Check the sugar content; most of the sugar is eaten during fermentation, but some have added sugars after fermentation is complete. If they are stored out of the fridge, they will continue fermenting, which reduces sugar content even more.

- **Focus on digestion**—Digestion is by far the most important part of health. The amount of energy we have depends largely on how we digest our food (the more energy we use digesting, the less we have available to use). We need to keep a good balance of bacteria in our gut, and do everything we can to assist our bodies with digestion. The above points are all great for good digestion. Also, try to avoid eating when you are upset.

- **Eat breakfast**—The most important time to eat protein and fat is in the morning. Many people skip breakfast because they don't feel like eating, but it is essential to have a good breakfast. It sets you up for the day, keeps your blood sugar stable, and helps balance pH. Avoid eating fruit or other sweet things for breakfast because it can upset your blood sugar. The best time to eat fruit or sweets is after a good lunch or dinner (and with fat).

  Take the time to sit down and eat (don't eat breakfast on the run). Eggs are the easiest and quickest meal to make in the mornings and will give you enough protein and fat to start your day adequately.

- **Eat plenty of protein**—Include a good portion of protein at each meal (three times a day). The easiest and best sources of protein are eggs, meats, and poultry. Fish is okay occasionally if you are healthy, but while you are getting your body back into balance, it is better avoided. It is a wonderful food, but the oceans are full of toxins. Get your omega 3 fatty acids from fish oil.

  It is very difficult to get adequate protein and fat from a vegetarian diet, but is possible if you can live with eating a serving of eggs at least twice a day and a lot of butter and coconut oil. Legumes can be used and are good sources of second-class protein, but are best served with a first-class protein (eggs, meat, or poultry).

  Make sure you use quality free-range meat, poultry, and eggs. The pastured animal products contain more nutrients, the right balance of fats, and also, the animals are treated humanely.

- **Eat plenty of fat**—Eat plenty of quality fats, especially butter and coconut oil. Eat your organic meat with the fat on. All oils and fats need to be kept below their smoking points to keep their healthy structure intact. Butter and coconut oil have a much higher smoking point, so are better for cooking.

- **Enjoy vegetables**—Vegetables add variety and texture to a LCHF diet. However, contrary to popular belief, they are not essential, so if you or your children do not like vegetables, it is much more important to eat enough quality protein and fat. Many traditional healthy cultures ate no vegetables at all and they were superbly healthy. For example, the Inuit did not have access to vegetables, and the Masai considered vegetables to be "food for cows." What few people know is that protein and fat are extremely nutrient dense, much more so than plant foods. If we start our day with eggs and butter, we have already packed ourselves full of vitamins A, B, D, E, K, iron, Zinc, calcium, lecithin, iodine and more. If we include a side of tomato, then we have added vitamin C to the list. And, if we add quality salt, we add over 80 more minerals!

  In addition, the fat soluble vitamins in vegetables are not available for assimilation if we don't eat fat. Sautéing vegetables in butter or adding butter is the perfect way to eat vegetables.

The greatness of a nation and its moral progress can be judged by the way its animals are treated.

GANDHI

- **Limit fructose from fruit and sweets to under 15 g a day**—In our natural diet, we would have consumed very low levels of fructose (the natural sugar in fruit and honey). Too much fructose can also lead to dangerous health conditions, including weight gain and diabetes—our liver can only handle a limited amount. Try to keep your fructose from fruit and sweets under 15 g a day. If you follow the advice in the following sections about limiting fruit and healthy sweets, then your levels of fructose will be fine. One tsp of honey contains approximately 4 g of fructose. Stevia contains no fructose. Here is a table of the fructose in the most popular fruits:

Fresh Fruit	Serving size	Grams of fructose
Limes	1 medium	0
Lemon	1 medium	0.6
Cranberries	1 cup	0.7
Passion fruit	1 medium	0.9
Plum	1 medium	1.2
Apricot	1 medium	1.3
Guava	2 medium	2.2
Cantaloupe/rockmelon, cubed	1 cup	2.9
Raspberries	1 cup	3.0
Clementine	1 medium	3.4
Kiwi fruit	1 medium	3.4
Blackberries	1 cup	3.5
Star fruit	1 medium	3.6
Cherries, sweet	10	3.8
Cherries, sour	1 cup	4.0
Strawberries	1 cup	3.8
Pineapple	1 slice	4.0
Grapefruit, pink or red	½ medium	4.3
Boysenberries	1 cup	4.6
Tangerine/mandarin	1 medium	4.8
Nectarine	1 medium	5.4
Peach	1 medium	5.9
Orange, navel	1 medium	6.1

Fresh Fruit	Serving size	Grams of fructose
Papaya	½ medium	6.3
Honey dew melon, cubed	1 cup	7
Banana	1 medium	7.1
Blueberries	1 cup	7.4
Apple	1 medium	9.5
Persimmon	1 medium	10.6
Watermelon, diced	1 cup	5
Pear	1 medium	11.8
Mango	½ medium	16.2
Grapes, red or green	1 cup	12.4

Dried fruit	Serving size	Grams of fructose
Prune	6 medium	7.2
Apricots	½ cup	8.2
Raisins/sultanas	¼ cup	12.3
Dates	6 medium	15.6
Figs	½ cup	11.5

- **Limit fruit to two servings daily**—Eat a variety of fruits, but stick to the non-sweet varieties most of the time. For example, apples, berries, pineapple, papaya, or kiwi fruit. Oranges and bananas can be eaten less often but are too sweet to be a daily part of the diet. We often share a banana between the four of us as part of a fruit salad. Always eat fruit after a meal that included protein and fat. Eating sweets and fruit with fat reduces the glucose response, so a dollop of cream on your fruit is a perfect combination. The same goes for potato or other carbohydrates; always eat them with fat.

- **Enjoy healthy sweets in moderation**—Enjoy healthy sweets but don't overdo it. If you eat too many, it will prevent your health from improving. Use fruit for every-day sweetness. A fruit salad with cream is a beautiful daily dessert.

Be wary of what you eat—the diseases that result from overindulging are not worth the temporary satisfaction you get from that sugary meal or snack.

NANCY APPLETON, PHD, SUICIDE BY SUGAR

Some of the desserts are sweetened with raw honey. Limit raw honey to no more than one tsp in a day. A serving of any of the desserts in this book will keep you under one tsp of honey. Dried fruits are also used to sweeten some of the desserts; they are very sweet, and should also be used in moderation.

- **Avoid juices**—Juice is very high in fructose, especially commercial juice. Most are made from concentrate and contain over 15 g of fructose in a single serve. For special occasions, I make pine lime punch with fresh pineapple pureéd in the food processor, lime juice, mineral water, and a dash of stevia. It goes down as a treat at children's parties. Each serve only contains a few grams of fructose.

- **Drink filtered water**—Tap water is contaminated with many chemicals, including heavy metals, chlorine and, in most places, fluoride. Again, the mainstream health industry tells us that fluoride is safe, and makes our teeth strong, but it is a poison that causes many illnesses, including bone loss, cancer, and fluorosis. Some water filters (such as ceramic or compressed carbon filters) remove most of the toxins, and leave the water's minerals intact, but are unable to remove fluoride. The best system to use (if your water is fluoridated) is reverse osmosis. Try to find a good system that re-mineralises the water.

The mainstream health industry also tells us to drink eight glasses of water a day, and more if we exercise. This is a very new idea, recently introduced into Western society. Ancient traditions and eastern medicine have never advocated the 8 by 8 theory. Some people sip water all day long to try and reach their quota, but this can cause stress on the kidneys and dilute the level of salt in the blood, which affects the brain, muscle, and heart tissue. It is important to be hydrated, but it is better to listen to your body. The theory that once you are thirsty, you are already dehydrated doesn't make sense. Our body gives us signals about what we need, and those signals are there for a reason; just as the hunger signal tells us when we need to eat. It is better to drink when you first rise (to rehydrate after sleep) and then drink when you are thirsty (away from meals). It will naturally be less in winter, more in summer, less when sedentary, and more when exercising.

Avoid using plastic water bottles, including the polycarbonate bottles that are advertised as a healthier option. Even polycarbonate releases dangerous chemicals into your water. Try to use glass or stainless steel.

- **Eat spices and quality salt**—Herbs, spices and salt are full of minerals, and aid digestion. Fresh is always best if you can get it. Salt is another real food that has been attacked by the mainstream health industry. It is true that the copious amounts of sodium used in processed food are bad for you. However, unprocessed salt is not only okay, but essential to a balanced diet. Salt helps to digest proteins, and is a valuable source of minerals. Use an unprocessed salt, like pink Himalayan salt or rock salt. Sea salt is no longer a good choice because of the amount of heavy metals and other chemicals present in the oceans.

- **Take fish oil daily**—Fish oil is a super-food, and a must for the developing brains of children. Use bottled fish oil that hasn't been processed. The best in Australia is Melrose or Metagenics; they are specially packaged in the absence of light, which helps the oil retain its nutritional value, and keeps the oil from oxidizing. It is kept in a special cardboard box or dark bottle to keep it from oxidizing after you purchase it. Any fish oil not kept away from light is no longer any good, and needs to be avoided.

- **Prepare bone broths**—Bone broths are a digestive aid, are full of minerals, and have been proven to help with intestinal disorders, cancer, bone disorders, arthritis, and asthma. They are also an old-fashioned remedy for the cold or flu. In addition to the health benefits, bone broths add a beautiful flavour to food. They can be used as a drink, or as the base for stocks, soups, and sauces. They are simple to make; every time you have a roast chicken, you can boil the bones with some apple cider vinegar. Or, you can purchase chicken frames (carcasses) from your organic butcher and make a broth with those.

- **Eliminate any problems with yeast or Candida**—Yeast is a problem for many people. Topical treatments for yeast issues like thrush, athletes' foot, and jock itch only treat the external symptoms. For many people, they are chronic conditions. Thrush and other yeast

The breakdown and decay process is largely due to yeast, bacteria, parasites, and fungi living off the body. In a healthy person, Candida albicans, other strains of yeast, and fungi exist in balance with normal intestinal flora or bacteria. Healthy flora are necessary for digestion, assimilation of nutrition, and the prevention of infection... Candida yeast can increase rapidly and overtake the normal, beneficial gut bacteria. This is largely due to the Western world's overuse of antibiotics, the side effects of birth control pills, and our dependence on starch-and sugar-laden diets. The gut flora becomes imbalanced and the yeast is allowed to proliferate out of control.

CAROLINE SUTHERLAND, THE BODY KNOWS HOW TO STAY YOUNG

related conditions are accepted as normal these days. They aren't. They are an indication that yeast and other bacteria in the gut have multiplied out of control. Yeast feeds on sugar and poor quality carbohydrates like white bread and pasta. To irradiate these issues, the yeast must be killed internally. Changing to a healthier diet will kill the yeast over a period of time. Also, eat plenty of cold-pressed coconut oil (it is antimicrobial) and include raw garlic in your diet (it is antifungal). Include plenty of cultured food or a therapeutic strength probiotic. To kill the yeast quickly, for a period of six or eight weeks, eliminate all forms of sweetness (including fruit) and eliminate grains.

- **Ensure you eliminate well**—Constipation is a big problem for some people, and is a serious health issue because toxins re-absorb into the body instead of being eliminated. It is important to have at least one bowel movement a day, and ideally, two or three.

  Avoid laxatives and fibre supplements. Contrary to popular belief, large amounts of insoluble fibre damage the bowel by putting holes in the lining. Those lacerations produce mucus and that is how everything passes through and makes us 'regular.' In fact, in most cases, it is this fibre damage that has caused the constipation problems in the first place. And, because we become more and more fibre dependent, we can become constipated when we switch to LCHF; not because the diet is bad for us, but because of the fibre damage.

  In these cases, the bowel needs support. Take special care to increase your fat intake. Fat is incredibly nourishing for the bowel and works a treat for many people. If the issue continues, powdered magnesium works for most people because it draws water to the bowel, and is the easiest way to get things moving without damaging the bowel. Another brilliant product, developed by an Australian naturopath, is called Life capsules, and supports the bowel working the way it should. The adult dose is too strong for some people, so they find they are better on the children's dose. These can be purchased from Living Valley Springs Health Retreat.

  If you have had issues with your bowel for a while, it is a good idea to have colonic irrigation to remove all the hardened faecal matter. Each person who has had elimination issues can have up to 5kg of old faecal matter stuck in the bowel. Once it is removed, if you keep it moving, and you eat well, it won't build up again.

Also, sitting on the toilet is an unnatural position and puts a large kink in the bowel; we are designed to squat. To fix this problem, keep a fairly tall stool in the bathroom that allows you to bring your knees up to your chest.

In addition, Eastern medicine has known for centuries that the mind and body are intricately connected. The emotional connection that leads to constipation is usually fear of change, holding on to the past, and being unable to let go. We are literally holding on to our, excuse the word, 'crap'. Many practitioners use the saying, 'Tight mind, tight colon.' And, it is very true. Daily meditation helps with the process of letting go.

- **Get outside every day**—Try and get 15 minutes of sunshine every day. This will benefit you in many ways. Sunshine (without sunglasses) produces the right balance of serotonin and melatonin, which lifts our mood during the day and helps us sleep better at night. Sunshine also provides adequate levels of vitamin D, which is one of the most essential nutrients for great health and vitality, but only if you don't wash the exposed skin with soap or other cleansers. Washing with soap removes the oil that converts the sunlight to vitamin D. All those freshly scrubbed children who run out in the sun every day can actually be lacking in vitamin D, because they never have natural oils on their skin. We don't need to scrub our entire bodies; just the smelly parts. In addition, avoiding soap and other cleansers keeps your skin youthful and moist. Removing all your natural oils takes away your skin's natural protection and encourages pre-mature ageing.

- **Make good sleep a priority**—Stressed lifestyles push our stress hormone (cortisol) up, which can then interfere with sleep patterns. Also, our deep sleep occurs before midnight, so going to bed late interferes with our hormones. Why does it matter if we have too much cortisol? For a few reasons, but one of them is that it prevents weight loss. Too much cortisol prompts our body to store fat, particularly around the middle.

Come forth into the light of things; let Nature be your teacher.

WILLIAM WORDSWORTH

- **Meditate daily if you can**—Meditation reduces cortisol levels (stress hormones) during the day, and keeps you relaxed. You can choose to do long meditations, but there are many short meditations that you can buy on iTunes, and 10 minutes is all you need to completely change your mood and eliminate stress.

- **Learn how to breathe well**—If you watch a baby, she will naturally breathe with her diaphragm, which means she breathes down to her belly (the belly will rise and fall with her breath). Most people have forgotten how to breathe well, and their breath is short and sharp, into their chest, often through the mouth. Mouth breathing and over-breathing contribute to many health issues including allergies, asthma, anxiety, digestive disorders, crooked teeth, and many more. Fixing your breathing pattern will have a dramatic impact on your health.

  Natural breath is slow, through the nose, and into the belly. Learning how to breathe well again is easy to do. The easiest way to get started is to lie down, put your hands on your belly, and try to get your lungs to come down when you breathe; imagine they are massaging the internal organs in your belly. Then try it sitting and standing. As you move through your day, when you remember, focus on your breath going deep into your belly. After practising for a while, you will naturally breathe into your belly, and it will feel good.

  If you have children, encourage them to close their mouth, especially while watching television, which is often when the mouth starts to hang open.

- **Eliminate toxins**—We store toxins in our fat cells to protect ourselves. Eliminating toxins from skin care products and household cleaners is a great way to boost weight loss and general health.

- **Enjoy your food!**—I love and nourish my body, and I love to eat. I really love good food. Initially, it is a big adjustment to change eating habits, but the rewards are truly satisfying in every way. Not only will you feel better, but real food tastes far superior to convenience food. It has beautiful rich flavours, and is a joy to eat. It is like eating at a fancy restaurant as opposed to a fast-food restaurant. There is no question which food will taste better. The contrast between processed convenience food and real food is much the same. Treat yourself!

Making a change

All this information at once can be difficult to process and might be overwhelming. Don't feel that you have to get it perfect overnight. You can start improving things one thing at a time, and eventually, you will get to everything. The initial change is a bit of work, but once you have new pantry items, and have located local organic grocery stores or delivery places, it is so easy to cook this way. The reason I developed these recipes was not to write a book, but to make my life easier. I needed quick, easy, nutritious meals, that weren't complicated to make.

It is also easier if we avoid becoming overly compulsive about it. Some people have a very strong reaction to hearing this information, and want to change their family's diet immediately, which is great, but they can then put a lot of pressure on their family members to change right away. If the family hasn't been eating a perfect diet up to this point, slowly eliminating certain foods and adding new ones is not going to hurt them. A few extra months isn't going to make that much difference. It is wonderful to take the opportunity to change to a natural diet, which is more nurturing, but relax and enjoy the journey. Take things one step at a time.

After my children were a certain age, and I knew they were well educated about food, I let them make their own food choices when they were confronted with an option outside of the home. This can be difficult to do, but is better for them in the long run. When my son started grade 8, he had access to the tuckshop. He went crazy for a full year, but would always come home and talk to me about it. He would say, "Mum, my body feels awful, but I can't stop myself." He eventually hated how he felt so much that he made his own decision to go back to a healthy diet, and that is so much more powerful than my forcing him.

> If hunger is not the problem, then eating is not the solution.
>
> **ANONYMOUS**

Here in Australia, children are tested by the government every two years to see if they are on target academically. Every time my daughter Anna had been tested prior to grade 5, she tested way above her grade level. When she was in grade 5, I received her results that showed her at a very average level. When I showed her the results, she pondered for a minute and then said, "Oh, I was eating jelly beans with [her friend]." She knew from my work that sugar impacts IQ levels temporarily and she put two and two together. She had been eating them for a few days, and even during the test! Her reading level had been tested a few weeks earlier and showed her reading at a grade 10 level. There is no doubt that the sugar had an impact on her results, and she knew that. It was a good opportunity for her to see this for herself.

Also, if you eat for emotional reasons, then I recommend reading *Women, Food and God* by Geneen Roth. Whether you are male or female, this book will help you figure out what prompts you to use food to numb your emotions or distract yourself from life. It has been helping millions free themselves from the emotional turmoil of eating for the wrong reasons.

Stocking the pantry

To make things easier, here is a list of pantry items that are used in this cookbook, and where they can be purchased. Some of the products are harder to source, so to make things easier, we are now stocking some items on our websites or linking to good suppliers.

If your organic grocery store or delicatessen doesn't have any of the items listed, they are normally more than happy to order something in for you.

FOOD	DESCRIPTION / HINTS	WHERE TO PURCHASE
Activated nuts	Organic, activated nuts. Nuts are a fantastic snack and make great flours when ground. But, nuts and grains do contain natural chemicals like phytic acid and enzyme inhibitors, which are irritating to our digestive system. Soaking and dehydrating nuts and grains mimics the germination process, and breaks down these plant toxins. Activated nuts have been soaked and dehydrated.	*christinecronau.com/activated-nuts*
Almond meal or flour	Ground almonds. The healthiest almond meal is one you can make yourself from activated almonds. See above.	Organic grocery store or grind yourself in a processor, thermomix, or coffee grinder.
Apple cider vinegar	Available in supermarkets, but brands in the organic grocery stores should be raw and unprocessed. Braggs is a good brand.	Organic grocery store.
Arrowroot	Ground arrowroot, used to thicken sauces, or other mixtures. Arrowroot is sold in supermarkets, but contains a preservative.	Organic grocery store.
Besan flour	Finely ground chickpeas.	Organic grocery store.
Buckwheat flour	Buckwheat is not a grain; it is actually related to rhubarb, so is a great alternative to flours made from grain.	Organic grocery store.
Cacao butter (raw)	The solid fat extracted from cacao beans.	Organic grocery store. *christinecronau.com/chocolate*
Cacao mass (raw)	Raw cacao mass that is made from grinding cacao beans. Most organic grocery stores don't stock this, so we are now stocking it.	*christinecronau.com/chocolate*
Cacao powder (raw)	Choose organic, raw cacao. Commercial cocoa beans are treated with a lot of chemicals. Raw cacao hasn't been heated and contains more nutrients.	Organic grocery store.

FOOD	DESCRIPTION / HINTS	WHERE TO PURCHASE
Canned tomatoes	Our supermarket sells organic canned tomatoes, but they are also available at the organic grocery store.	Supermarket or organic grocery store.
Carob powder	Made from toasting and grinding the pods of a carob tree. Often used as a substitute for chocolate. Avoid solid carob because it has been made with skim milk powder.	Organic grocery store.
Chia seeds	A small seed that is packed with omega-3 fats and other goodies. They can be thrown onto salads, or stir-fries to add a boost of nutrition.	Organic grocery store.
Chips	There are recipes for home made chips in this book, but sometimes, packaged chips are a great option for a lunchbox treat or children's birthday party. Unfortunately, most are cooked in damaged, rancid seed oils. Woolworths Macro Organic brand sells sweet potato crisps, potato chips, and vegetable chips in sustainable palm oil.	Woolworths. Look for the plain chips; they are additive free.
Coconut cream	Use the coconut cream instead of coconut milk, which has had some of the fat removed. Most in the supermarket contain additives.	Organic grocery store.
Coconut flour	Finely ground coconut. Can be used in place of bread crumbs.	Any organic grocery store. Not all organic grocery stores stock so ask them to get it in.
Coconut oil	Extra-virgin, unprocessed.	*christinecronau.com/ coconut-oil*
Curry powder	The curry powder in the supermarket generally has additives.	Organic grocery store.
Desiccated coconut	Finely shredded coconut. Commercial coconut has an anti-caking agent.	Organic grocery store.

FOOD	DESCRIPTION / HINTS	WHERE TO PURCHASE
Dijon mustard	You can buy this at the supermarket if you check the ingredients. Most have sugar and additives, but a few don't. I get beautiful French mustard from the supermarket.	Supermarket or organic grocery store.
Dried apricots	Don't buy these in the supermarket. They are treated with chemicals to keep them bright orange.	Organic grocery store.
Dried cranberries	Most dried cranberries are made with sugar (even those available in organic grocery stores). Choose a brand made with apple juice (not apple juice concentrate).	Organic grocery store. If their brand has sugar, ask them to stock another one.
Extra-virgin olive oil and other oils	Make sure they are cold-pressed, which means they haven't been heated.	Organic grocery store or at some supermarkets.
Gelatine sheets	The powdered gelatine isn't as good and contains a preservative.	Organic grocery store.
Gherkins or cornichons	Pickled cucumbers.	Delicatessen.
Honey (raw)	Commercial honey is super-heated, which destroys the enzymes, and makes it toxic. Ensure the label says raw or unprocessed.	Organic grocery store.
Kombucha	Fermented drinks infuse the digestive system with lactobacilli, lactic acid, enzymes, and minerals. In fact, when we consume fermented products such as kombucha, we no longer need probiotics to balance the bacteria in our gut	Organic grocery store. *christinecronau.com/ kombucha*
Kuzu	Kuzu is a Japanese root, which acts as a fantastic thickening agent for stews, soups, and sweet dishes like stewed apple. Unlike highly processed corn starch, kuzu has health benefits, including alkalising the body.	Organic grocery store.

FOOD	DESCRIPTION / HINTS	WHERE TO PURCHASE
Oat bread	I am often asked about bread. Many people on LCHF don't eat bread, but some like to eat it occasionally. Most breads are damaging to the digestive system, especially the wheat family (including spelt, barley, and rye). Ancient Grains Oat Bread is much less inflammatory than other grain-based breads, and is a sour-dough, which makes it much more digestible (neutralises plant toxins). Grains and nuts are much more digestible if soaked or made into sour dough.	Organic grocery store. *facebook.com/ AncientGrainsBreads*
Organic salsa	Some organic grocery stores carry a good brand of salsa, that isn't made with sugar (check the ingredients).	Organic grocery store.
Organic sultanas	Make sure they don't contain vegetable oil.	Organic grocery store or at some supermarkets.
Palm oil	Like coconut oil, palm oil has been given a bad rap because of its high saturated fat content, however, for this reason, it is actually one of the better oils. But, it is important to source an environmentally friendly one. Elais sells a lovely palm oil, and is certified as pro forest.	*elaeisorganic.com*
Pasta sauce	If you can find an organic, quality pasta sauce, without sugar or other additives, it is an easy way to make a quick dinner by adding to beef mince.	Supermarket or organic grocery store.
Pepitas	Pumpkin seeds.	Organic grocery store.
Quality baking powder	The commercial baking powder in the supermarket contains chemicals.	Organic grocery store.
Salt	Buy an unprocessed salt like pink Himalayan or rock salt. Unprocessed sea salt was a great option, but because of the pollution in the oceans, it is better avoided.	Organic grocery store.

FOOD	DESCRIPTION / HINTS	WHERE TO PURCHASE
Stevia	The stevia plant is a small green herb, and its leaves are extremely sweet. The leaves are ground into a fine white powder. If you are in the US, it is only stocked in the supplement section of the health food store because the FDA has ruled it as unsafe as an additive but not unsafe as a supplement. Make sure the brand you use is pure stevia; otherwise some of the recipes will not work. The brand I use and reference in the recipes is Nirvana pure extract powder.	Organic grocery store. *christinecronau.com/stevia*
Sushi sheets	Sheets of dried seaweed.	Supermarket.
Tamari	Wheat-free soy sauce, that has been fermented the old-fashioned way. Commercial soy sauces should be avoided.	Organic grocery store.
Vanilla beans		Organic grocery store.
Wasabi	Powdered horseradish used for sushi. The wasabi available in supermarkets has green food colouring. Use the powdered version in organic grocery stores, which is coloured with spiralina.	Organic grocery store.

Herbs and spices

The herbs and spices used in this book are:

- Basil
- Bay leaves
- Cardamom pods (chai latte)
- Chilli powder
- Cinnamon
- Cinnamon sticks (chai latte)
- Course ground black pepper
- Cumin seeds
- Curry powder (turmeric, mustard seed, coriander seed, black pepper, garlic, ginger, hot paprika, and sweet paprika).
- Dill
- Dried coriander leaves
- Garam masala (pepper, caraway, fennel, cardamom, cinnamon, and clove)
- Garlic
- Ground coriander seeds
- Nutmeg
- Oregano
- Paprika (not the hot one)
- Rosemary
- Star anise
- Thyme

I like to keep organic fresh herbs in the garden (and kitchen window) so that they are always available for cooking and garnishing. This is not essential, but it is fun, and does make cooking easier.

Perishables

Food	Hints	Where to purchase
Butter	We buy quality farm butter from the markets. Try to find quality grass-fed butter. A strong yellow colour indicates that the butter is grass-fed. White butter is a sure sign that the cows are being grain fed.	Organic grocery store or market.
Milk	Buy quality milk, as unprocessed as possible. Make sure the milk is not homogenised. Homogenisation is a technique that prevents the cream particles from separating from the milk, but research shows that this process damages the fat particles. Also never drink any milk or consume any dairy containing milk solids. The cholesterol in milk solids (milk powder) is damaged and oxidised. Both these damaged fats increase risk for heart disease.	Organic grocery store or market.
Organic cream and sour cream	Again, as unprocessed as possible. I try to get all my dairy organic or from small dairy producers who grass feed their cattle.	Organic grocery store.
Organic yoghurt	The yoghurt at the organic grocery store won't be homogenised, which is a lot healthier.	Organic grocery store.
Organic frozen berries		Organic grocery store.
Grass-fed meat	Many supermarkets are now stocking grass-fed and organic meat. Or, find a good organic butcher. Our butcher gives us large discounts if we purchase in bulk. He puts the items in 500g bags so that we can put it all in the freezer, and pull out one packet at a time.	Some supermarkets or organic butcher.
Ham and bacon	Most ham and bacon is cured with sugar, nitrates, and a whole host of other chemicals. Purchase organic, nitrate-free ham and bacon.	Organic butcher or some delicatessens.

Keeping food wholesome

If we use beautiful, fresh, healthy ingredients, it is important to prepare them in a way that preserves their nutritional value.

AVOID MICROWAVES

Microwave ovens alter the structure of food. They destroy vitamins and minerals and change the structure of fats and proteins. Eating microwaved food causes changes in the blood similar to that when a patient is in early stages of cancer. The altered amino acids in milk can cause damage to the liver and nervous system, which is especially unfortunate for the many formula-fed babies whose parents use the microwave.

AVOID ALUMINIUM AND NON-STICK COOKWARE

Aluminium has been shown to cause Alzheimer's and other diseases; the aluminium used in cookware transfers very easily into food (aluminium is also found in all anti-perspirant deodorants, so try to find a natural one at the organic grocery store or simply use a bit of bi carb soda).

Non-stick cookware is coated with a substance that releases toxic fumes and chemicals when heated. Use stainless steel or cast iron instead.

KEEP OILS WELL BENEATH THEIR SMOKING POINTS

The structure of any oil changes when the oil is heated over its smoking point, causing free radicals to form and destroying the antioxidants. It also brings it too close to its flash point, which means it could catch fire and become dangerous. My sister is a nurse and she has told me about many deep-frying accidents; always use a thermometer when deep-frying, and only use a few centimetres of oil in the bottom of the pan.

Use quality oil. Vegetable oils, especially canola oil, are unhealthy and are already full of free radicals before they are heated. I have a friend who knows canola farmers who won't eat canola oil because they know what they have to

---

Today most of the fats in our diet are derived from vegetable oils (soy, corn, safflower, and canola), and it's almost impossible to find any products at the grocery store that don't contain them... These popular fats are very unhealthy. You see, so called light oils affect the cell walls' ability to process glucose, so the cells' ability to assimilate sugar and starch is lessened. It's bad enough that we have too much starch and sugar in our diets, but if our cell walls are weakened by the wrong kinds of fat, we aren't able to assimilate the starch and sugar at all.

CAROLINE SUTHERLAND, THE BODY KNOWS HOW TO STAY YOUNG

do to it when they produce it; they eat butter. Make sure your oils are cold-pressed (unrefined, extra-virgin).

The following are approximate smoking points for the oils I use:

OIL	SMOKING POINT °C	SMOKING POINT °F
Extra-virgin olive oil	160°C	320°F
Butter	177°C	350°F
Extra-virgin coconut oil	177°C	350°F
Lard	182°C	370°F

I never fry or sauté with olive oil because it is very easy to overheat without knowing; I always use coconut oil or butter. If I deep-fry, I use coconut oil. If I bake with olive oil, I always set the oven well below the smoking point (140°C or 150°C).

COOK VEGETABLES AL DENTÉ

To keep the nutrients in your vegetables, prevent them from overcooking. Cook them until they are only just cooked, so they still have very bright colours. Once they start to lose colour, they are overcooked. Serving vegetables with butter helps the fat-soluble vitamins become more available.

Utensils to help

These are a few of the kitchen utensils I find essential for making recipes easier.

THERMOMETER

If you can, purchase a good thermometer, digital if possible. Some recipes, such as pouring custard, are very tricky without a thermometer, but very easy with one. If you look at general recipes for making custards, they always include notes about not letting them get too hot, or they will split and curdle. It is very hard to figure

Fats and oils to be avoided, in addition to partially hydrogenated vegetable fats, include any rancid or over-heated fats and oils that contain break-down products, such as oxidized fatty acids, oxidized sterols, peroxides, acrolein, hydrocarbons, and aromatic compounds. These types of abused fats and oils are not safe. They range from immediately toxic to chronically toxic. Free radicals can form in polyunsaturated oils during industrial processing. These can interact with sulfhydryl groups in proteins as well as with unsaturated fatty acids and are very destructive of cell membranes.

MARY GENIG, PHD, KNOW YOUR FATS

out at exactly what point the eggs have cooked but are not hot enough to curdle. I have included the exact temperature in my recipe, so it is very easy to make. A thermometer is also essential for deep frying, so that oil can be kept at its healthiest (over-heating it destroys the antioxidants and produces free radicals).

If you are in the US, try to find a thermometer that displays both Celsius and Fahrenheit so that you don't need to convert the temperatures when making custard and chocolate (this book uses Celsius). My digital thermometer has a switch on it that allows me to switch between Celsius and Fahrenheit. If you do need to convert temperatures, a conversion table is included in the back of the book.

SCALES

I measure a lot of my ingredients in weight, so scales also make it easier to cook the recipes in this book. Again, if you are in the US, try to purchase scales that measure both grams and ounces, so you don't need to convert the measurements in the book.

FOOD PROCESSOR

Food processors make it so quick and easy to chop, blend, pureé, and more, so they are a tremendous help to have in the kitchen. A food processor is also essential to make your own mayonnaise and other salad dressings that require emulsification. They can make a very time-consuming recipe very quick and easy. For example, the carrot cake in the next section can be done without a processor, and is still a very easy recipe, but will be time-consuming because of all the grating.

Special notes before cooking

EGGS

All eggs used in the book are large.

OVEN TEMPERATURES

Oven temperatures vary greatly. If things are not browning, or if baked custard is not puffing, turn the temperature up. My oven has been tested and is at the correct temperature, but I find that a lot of domestic ovens run quite cool and can be 10°C or 20°C below temperature. When I was preparing these recipes for the photo shoot at the photographer's house, I had to run the oven 20°C higher than I normally do. Interestingly, it is a brand new, fan forced oven. If your oven is not fan forced, it will also cook around 20°C below temperature.

STEVIA

A big note about stevia. I use pure stevia in my recipes. Many times, people buy products from the supermarket with a large label that says 'Stevia' but if you read the fine print, it contains other ingredients like erythritol. These products are sometimes called granulated stevia. Pure stevia is extremely sweet, so is only used in very small quantities. ½ tsp is equivalent to one cup of sugar. These other products are made so that they are the same sweetness as sugar (that is, one cup of the stevia mix is equivalent to one cup of sugar). So, you could imagine what happens when these mixes are used in my recipes instead of pure stevia. The result is not going to be sweet at all. So, it is imperative to make sure that you are using pure stevia to achieve the desired result. I use Nirvana pure extract powder.

If you would like to use pure stevia in other recipes, ½ a tsp is equivalent to 1 cup of sugar.

There is a bitter component in the stevia leaf, but the better brands have removed that bitter component, so avoid the cheaper brands. Also, because stevia is so sweet, if it is overdone, it can taste artificial. If it is used in the right amounts, with the right flavours, it is a beautiful sweetener that doesn't spike blood glucose and has no fructose.

> He that takes medicine and neglects diet wastes the skill of the physician.
> **CHINESE PROVERB**

> Why are we here? We exist not to pursue happiness, which is fleeting, or outer accomplishment, which can always be bettered. We are here to nourish the self.
> **DEEPAK CHOPRA**

Early morning is the most important time to eat a large serving of protein with plenty of fat.

My favourite food for breakfast is eggs. Eggs are natures perfect food; easy to prepare, a first-class protein, and delicious. I normally have three fried eggs every morning, sometimes with vegetables on the side. But, if you would like more variety, there are many interesting things you can do with eggs.

A good breakfast makes a huge difference to your day, and will help you avoid those blood sugar lows that tempt you to reach for a sugary, mid-morning snack.

For a wonderful side dish in the morning, I love to sauté mushrooms and spinach in butter, and then drizzle with tamari.

BREAKFAST
IDEAS

POACHED EGGS WITH HOLLANDAISE

Preparation time: 10 minutes

2-3 eggs per person

1. Bring a pot of water to the boil. Make sure it is just a gentle boil.
2. Crack 2 or 3 eggs into the water, turn the burner off, and let the eggs sit for 4 to 4½ minutes (for soft yolks).
3. Remove the eggs, place on a towel to drain excess water, then serve.

Easy hollandaise

120 g salted butter

2 egg yolks

1 tbsp lemon juice (approximately half a lemon)

1. Place the egg yolks and lemon in a food processor.
2. Melt the butter, and ensure it is still hot.
3. Process the egg yolk and lemon and gradually pour hot butter into the processor while processing.
4. Leave the processor running for five minutes while you poach the eggs to allow the sauce to thicken.

Since eggs have the highest amount of cholesterol per unit weight of all common foods (liver and brains have more), people began to fear them. Once called nature's most perfect food by nutritionists, eggs fell into disfavour and their consumption began to plummet after 1950. The average number of eggs consumed in the U.S. per person per year dropped from 389 in 1950... to only 234 in 1989. Americans today are eating many fewer eggs today than at the turn of the century... Thousands of egg farmers have gone out of business over the last 30 years because of the false dietary cholesterol scare. And millions of Americans have given up or substantially reduced their consumption of one of the best and most economic foods available for no good scientific or common sense reasons.

RUSSELL L. SMITH, PHD, HEALTH FREEDOM NEWS

FRIED EGGS WITH ZUCCHINI AND SWEET POTATO FRITTER

Preparation time: 10 minutes

Serves: 4

1 small sweet potato, grated

1 small zucchini, grated

2 tbsp of buckwheat flour

3 eggs for the fritter

Eggs for frying

1. Lightly whisk the egg.
2. Add the sweet potato and zucchini and mix.
3. Add the flour and stir until well combined.
4. Heat approximately one tbsp butter in a frying pan, and add large spoonfuls of the mixture.
5. Once browned on one side, turn fritters over, lightly press until flat, and continue cooking until the other side is golden brown.
6. While the fritters are cooking, fry the eggs in a separate pan. Serve eggs on the fritter and a bed of baby spinach or other greens.

Many cultures recognise that eggs are a brain food and encourage pregnant and nursing mothers to eat as many as possible. In China, nursing mothers who can afford it eat up to ten eggs per day! Unfortunately, most commercial eggs available in the supermarkets are inferior, nutritionally speaking, to the eggs from free-range hens of yesteryear. The typical supermarket egg from battery hens given grain feed contains nineteen more omega-six fatty acids than omega-3 fatty acids. Studies have shown that hens fed flax meal or fish meal rich in omega-3 fatty acids have equal amounts of omega-6 and omega-3, a very beneficial balance. Eggs from hens allowed to eat bugs and graze on green pasture would also have this favourable balance.

SALLY FALLON, NOURISHING TRADITIONS

SPANISH OMELETTE

Preparation time: 10 minutes

Serves: 4

Makes: 2 omelettes

8 eggs, lightly beaten

2 small potatoes, sliced

1 onion, chopped

3 tbsp butter

1. Melt a tbsp of the butter in a skillet, and sauté the onions.

2. Add the onions to the eggs, mix, and set aside.

3. Melt a tbsp of butter in the skillet, cover the bottom of the pan with half the potato slices, and cook on low heat for 5 minutes.

4. Turn the potato over, and cook for another 5 minutes (or until soft).

5. Add half the egg mixture, gently spreading it over the potato (try to leave the slices sticking to the bottom of the pan).

6. Cook until the egg on the edge of the pan has cooked a little.

7. Place under the grill on medium heat until the top of the omelette is cooked.

8. Cook a second omelette with the remaining potato and egg mixture.

9. Use a spatula to loosen the omelette from the pan, flip in half, cut into slices, and serve.

TIP: Use sweet potato and no onions for a delicious variation. This dish is also great for a quick dinner.

Good fats (animal fats, coconut oil, cold-pressed olive oil, etc) keep the skin moist and supple. People have the best intentions when reducing fat in the diet, but low-fat diets cause premature ageing and other health issues. The first signs of ageing show in the face, and are a good indication of the ageing occurring within the body. Reintroducing fat into the diet will slow the ageing process, and even reverse some of the effects of the previous diet.

MOROCCAN BAKED EGGS

Preparation time: 30 minutes

Serves: 4

1 large red onion

1 capsicum

4 cloves garlic, minced

2 tsp paprika (smoked, not hot)

2 sprigs thyme, leaves picked

Salt to taste

2 bottles or cans of diced tomatoes (350 or 400g)

8 eggs

4 tbsp butter

1 bunch asparagus (optional)

Gouda cheese, grated (enough to top each dish)

1. Pre-heat oven to 150°C (170°C if oven is not fan forced).
2. Sauté onion for around a minute.
3. Add the capsicum and garlic, and sauté until onion is soft.
4. Add paprika, thyme, and salt.
5. Add the tomatoes, stir well, and cook until mixture has reduced into a thick sauce.
6. Remove from the heat, add the butter, and stir until melted.
7. Place the mixture into 4 individual baking dishes.
8. Use a spoon to make a hollow in the mixture.
9. Crack two eggs into the hollow in each dish.
10. Bake in the oven for 15 minutes (or until the egg white is set, but the yolk is still soft).
11. While the eggs are baking, pan fry the asparagus in butter (add garlic if desired) for approximately 2 minutes, or until al dente.
12. Garnish the egg dishes with cheese, and asparagus.

So what is it about [saturated fat] that is so deadly? Frankly, I'm the wrong person to ask, because I don't happen to think that saturated fats are in any way damaging or dangerous. If they were, they wouldn't taste so damn delicious. Nature tends to warn us off dangerous foods by making them taste bitter or icky. Or giving them a bright-red colour.

DR MALCOLM KENDRICK, THE GREAT CHOLESTEROL CON

ITALIAN FRITTATA

Preparation time: 30 minutes

Serves: 4 to 6

1 potato, thinly sliced

1 onion, diced

1 clove garlic, minced

1 large tomato, diced

1 tsp paprika

1 zucchini, grated

A few sprigs of thyme, leaves picked (or a sprinkle of dried)

9 eggs, lightly beaten

300 ml cream

1 cup cheese, grated

Salt

1. Preheat oven to 130°C (150°C if oven is not fan forced).

2. Fry the sliced potato in butter for a few minutes.

3. Add the onion and fry until onion is soft.

4. Add the garlic, salt and herbs and stir.

5. Add the tomato and zucchini, and cook until slightly softened.

6. In a bowl, whisk eggs and cream, add the vegetables, and give the mixture a gentle mix with a fork.

7. Pour into a baking dish, sprinkle the grated cheese on top, and bake for around 40 minutes or until the egg mixture is firm and golden.

It is nigh impossible to eat enough cholesterol to meet your daily cholesterol needs. In order to meet this gap, the liver has to produce four or five times as much cholesterol as you ingest. In fact, you would need to eat about six to eight egg yolks each and every day to meet your daily requirement. As most of us never do that, the liver fills the gap.

DR MALCOLM KENDRICK, THE GREAT CHOLESTEROL CON

DEVILLED EGGS

Preparation time: 10 minutes

Serves: 4

8 eggs

2 or 3 tbsp mayonnaise (page 90)

Salt and pepper

1. Boil the eggs for 8 minutes, stirring occasionally to keep the yolks in the centre.
2. Remove the eggs from the heat, discard the hot water, and replace with cold (room-temperature) water.
3. Peel immediately.
4. Slice in half, and remove all yolks.
5. Mash the yolks with a fork.
6. Add the mayonnaise, salt, and pepper. Mix into a smooth paste.
7. Add the yolk mixture back into the eggs, and garnish with paprika.

An adequate supply of clean-burning food-fuel for the human engine is so absolutely fundamental both for health and for efficiency—we are so literally what we have eaten—that to be well fed is in very fact two-thirds of the battle of life from a physiological point of view.

DR WOODS HUTCHINSON, A HANDBOOK OF HEALTH

Snacks and lunches provide the biggest temptation to revert to convenience food. However, it is quite easy to take a little more time in the morning to prepare something nutritious.

When I am at home on my own, I often make a quick stir fry and add egg or leftover meat. It only takes a few minutes, and tastes much better than what you could buy at a food stall.

If you have children, and they are attending a party or other social event where commercial food will be served, it is also easy to make an alternative at home, like home-made chips.

SNACKS & LIGHT MEALS

Sweet potato crisps

Preparation time: 10 minutes

Serves: 4

2 large sweet potatoes

Coconut oil (enough to cover 3 cm of a small saucepan)

Paprika

Salt

1. With a quality vegetable peeler, peel the sweet potato, and continue to peel the sweet potato lengthways until the entire sweet potato is in long, thin strips.
2. Heat the oil in a small saucepan, until it reaches 160°C. **Note:** Don't let the oil exceed 170°C or it will go past its smoking point and be damaged.
3. Cook the sweet potato in small batches, stirring occasionally to avoid the chips sticking together.
4. Remove the crisps once they are very slightly brown (when the oil reaches 155 to 160°C again).
5. Place the crisps on a paper towel and sprinkle with paprika and salt.

Waffle potato chips

Preparation time: 20 minutes

Serves: 4

4 Large potatoes

Coconut oil (enough to cover 3 cm of a small saucepan)

Salt

1. Use a mandolin with a crinkle cut blade.
2. To achieve the waffle cut, slice the potato in one direction, turn 180° and slice in the other direction.
3. Heat the oil in a small saucepan until it reaches 165°C. **Note:** Don't let the oil exceed 170°C or it will go past its smoking point and be damaged.
4. Cook in small batches, stirring to ensure they are all covered by the bubbling oil and are not sticking. .
5. Once they are golden brown (when the oil reaches 160 to 165°C again), remove, place on a paper towel, and sprinkle with salt.

VEGETABLE PAKORAS

Preparation time: 10 minutes

Serves: 4

Free radicals are present in cheap vegetable oils like canola, and the numerous bottles in the supermarket labelled "Cholesterol Free." The level of free radicals present in these oils increases astronomically when they are used for deep frying, especially when the oil is heated to very high temperatures over and over again. Free radicals cause oxidative damage, which creates inflammation in the body. The inflammation damages cells and results in premature ageing. If you do need to buy commercial chips occasionally for a children's birthday, use a plain, unflavoured chip that is cooked in sustainable palm oil. Avoid all commercial chips cooked in vegetable oil.

1 large onion, sliced

50 g baby spinach

1¼ cup chickpea (besan) flour

1 tsp salt

¼ tsp chilli powder

½ tsp garam masala

1 tsp cumin seeds

½ tsp ground coriander seeds

1 tsp dried coriander leaves

¾ cup water

Coconut oil (enough to cover 3 cm of a small saucepan)

1. Mix the flour, salt, and spices.
2. Gradually add the water while mixing and mix into a smooth, thick paste.
3. Separate the onion into rings and place into the batter with the spinach.
4. Coat onion and spinach with the batter, and gather a cluster of onion rings and spinach leaves to make each pakora.
5. Heat the oil to 160°C. **Note:** Don't let the oil exceed 170°C or it will go past its smoking point and be damaged.
6. Fry one or two pakoras at a time until they are golden brown (approximately 4 minutes). Turn them over halfway through cooking.
7. Drain on paper towels and serve. Sprinkle with salt.

POTATO & CORN FRITTERS

Preparation time: 15 minutes

Serves: 4

1 large potato, grated

3 eggs

1 onion, diced

1 cob of corn, steamed (optional)

1 tomato, diced

150 to 200 g ham (organic, nitrate-free)

2 tbsp buckwheat flour

1 tbsp butter for frying

1. Mix the potato and egg in a large mixing bowl.

2. Add the remaining ingredients and mix well.

3. Heat approximately 1 tbsp of butter in a frying pan, and add large spoonfuls of the mixture.

4. Once browned on one side, turn fritters over, lightly press until flat, and continue cooking until the other side is lightly browned.

This is a lunchbox favourite for my children.

To keep the body in good health is a duty, otherwise we shall not be able to keep our mind strong and clear.

BUDDHA

CAULIFLOWER SUSHI

NOTE: Any fillings can be used, but these are my favourites.

Preparation time: 30 minutes

Serves: 4 to 6

1 cauliflower (around 1 kg)

60 g butter

2 tbsp brown rice vinegar

1 tsp raw honey

1 tbsp wasabi powder (use a natural one) (optional) .

1 Lebanese cucumber, sliced around 1 cm thick

1 avocado, sliced around 1 cm thick

I packet of sushi sheets

Sushi mat (for rolling the sushi)

Tamari

Looking for healthy, fun party food? Parties, especially children's parties, are no longer a challenge with LCHF. My favourite party foods include crumbed chicken, sushi, chips, fruit, watermelon, and ice cream cake. Favourites for both adults and children, guests will have absolutely no clue they have just been served healthy party food.

1. Cut the cauliflower in half, remove the stalk, break into pieces and place into a food processor.

2. Pulse the cauliflower until it resembles rice (this may have to be done in two batches).

3. Melt the butter in a frying pan, add the cauliflower rice and cook for approximately 6 minutes, stirring continuously.

4. Place the vinegar and honey into a small dish, and stir until honey is dissolved.

5. Place the cauliflower in a bowl, add the vinegar and honey, and stir will until the vinegar mixture is dispersed throughout the cauliflower. Allow to cool slightly.

6. Place a sushi sheet on the mat, shiny side down.

7. Place a few spoonfuls of cauliflower on the sheet, and spread and flatten with a spoon until the sheet is covered with a thin layer (leave around 6 cm at the bottom).

8. Mix the wasabi powder with a little water to make a paste, then spread a very thin line of paste around 4 cm from the top.

9. Place a strip of cucumber and avocado over the paste.

10. Use the mat to carefully roll the sushi, applying very gentle pressure as you roll. Give the roll a light squeeze once it is completely rolled. Set aside and repeat for remaining sushi rolls.

11. Let the rolls sit for around 10 minutes (helps the end to join and the sheet to soften).

12. Cut the sushi. To get even slices, first cut in half, then cut each half in half, and then each quarter in half.

13. Drizzle with tamari, or dip into a dish of tamari once served.

MEAT PATTIES WITH YOGHURT DIP

Preparation time: 15 minutes

Serves: 4

500 g chicken or beef mince

1 egg (not necessary when using chicken mince)

1 tsp powdered cumin

2 cloves garlic, minced

2 tsp fresh coriander, finely chopped (optional)

Butter or coconut oil for frying

Yoghurt for dipping

1. Place all ingredients into a large bowl and knead together with hands.

2. Roll into patties.

3. Melt the butter or oil in a frying pan and fry on both sides until cooked through and golden brown.

4. Serve with plain yoghurt (to add extra colour, add a little fresh coriander to the yoghurt).

Fat is your friend! Cholesterol forms vital corticosteroids, which are hormones that help us deal with stress and protect our bodies against heart disease and cancer. Cholesterol is also a precursor to the sex hormones and androgen, testosterone, estrogen, and progesterone...Fats in the diet provide energy, along with that satiated, not-hungry feeling. In addition, fats act as carriers for several fat-soluble vitamins, including A, D, E, and K; and the assumption that we should reduce their intake could lead to a number of metabolic imbalances.

CAROLINE SUTHERLAND, THE BODY KNOWS HOW TO STAY YOUNG

HAM AND PINEAPPLE PIZZA

This recipe takes a bit of time, but it is well worth the effort! Pizza has to be one of my favourite indulgences, and the cauliflower base makes it a great part of a LCHF lifestyle..

Preparation time: 1 hour

Serves: 4 to 6

1 cauliflower (around 1.2 kilos without its leaves)

1 cup parmesan cheese

3 eggs

3 tbsp almond meal

Salt (to taste)

1 tub or bottle of tomato paste (170 to 200g)

1 tbsp fresh oregano (1 tsp dried)

250 to 300 g mozzarella cheese

½ pineapple, chopped, drained, and patted dry in a cloth

150 g organic, nitrate-free ham, patted dry in a cloth and chopped

1. Pre-heat the oven to 150°C (170°C if oven is not fan forced).

2. Cut the cauliflower in half, remove the stalk, break into pieces and place into a food processor.

3. Pulse the cauliflower until it resembles rice (this may have to be done in two batches).

4. Place cauliflower into a large baking dish and spread it out so it is fairly flat.

5. Bake for around 30 minutes (remove half way through, stir, spread out again and place back in the oven).

6. Remove from the oven, taste the cauliflower to make sure it is cooked, place into a clean dish cloth, and allow to cool (around 20 minutes).

7. Once cool enough to handle, gather the ends of the towel so the cauliflower is in the middle of the towel. Twist the towel, and squeeze to remove as much liquid as possible. Quite a lot of liquid will come out, so keep squeezing!

8. Place what is left of the cauliflower into a bowl, add the parmesan, salt, and mix well.

9. Add the egg and almond meal, and knead together with hands until a smooth dough is formed (it will be slightly wet), and roll into a ball.

10. Line a pizza or baking tray with parchment paper, place the dough on the paper, and spread gently with fingers to make a circle shape. The edges can be left slightly thicker to form a crust, but it is not necessary.

11. Place the pizza base in the oven for 15 minutes. Half way through, flip the base over so both sides are cooked evenly.

12. While the base is cooking, make the pizza sauce by mixing the tomato paste with the oregano and 3 tbsp of filtered water.

13. Once pizza base is golden, remove from the oven and turn over again so it is right side up.

14. Spread the pizza sauce on the base and top with most of the ham, the cheese, the rest of the ham, then pineapple. Note: Any toppings can be used.

15. Return to the oven. To keep the base from becoming moist, slide the parchment paper and the base off the pizza tray, directly onto the oven rack. Cook for approximately 10 minutes, or until cheese is melted and slightly golden.

16. Slide the parchment paper back onto the pizza tray and transfer to a baking rack. Let it rest for 2 minutes, then slice.

BUCKWHEAT CREPES

These are simple crepes that make perfect wraps for savoury dishes and also beautiful desserts, such as a berry crepe filled with dollops of fresh cream.

Preparation time: 20 minutes

Serves: 4

4 eggs

½ cup buckwheat flour

1 cup filtered water

Pinch salt

Coconut oil or duck fat (for cooking)

1. Preheat a cast iron skillet to medium heat (or a healthy non-stick fry pan).
2. Beat the eggs with a whisk until egg yolk and white are well combined.
3. Add the water and whisk.
4. Add the dry ingredients and whisk until smooth.
5. Using a pastry brush, oil the pan.
6. Using a large serving spoon, pour the batter into the pan (approximately ¼ cup for each crepe).
7. Tilt the pan in a circular motion so the thin batter coats the surface evenly.
8. Cook for approximately one minute, then loosen with a spatula, and flip to cook for another minute or so.
9. Place cooked crepes into a tea towel, and if using later, store in an air tight container.

TIPS: Contrary to popular belief, crepes are very easy to make. If you end up with holes in the crepe, just fill them in with some extra batter. Use refined coconut oil so it doesn't overheat (refined coconut oil has a much higher smoking point).

Some buckwheat flour is stronger in taste than others (especially if it is not fresh). Shop around until you find a good one that is light in colour and very mild in flavour.

BUNLESS BURGERS WITH HORSERADISH DRESSING

Preparation time: 30 minutes

Serves: 4

Burgers

500 g mince

1 egg

1 tsp salt

Pepper to taste

Butter or coconut oil for frying

100 g Gouda cheese, sliced

Iceberg lettuce leaves

1 large tomato, sliced

1 large avocado, sliced

Dill pickles, thinly sliced

1 large red onion, thinly sliced into rings

1. Combine mince, egg, salt and pepper in a bowl and knead well with hands.
2. Shape the mince mixture into four burger patties.
3. On medium heat, fry the patties in butter or coconut oil.
4. While the burger patties are frying, fry the onion rings in butter until soft, then set aside.
5. After around 5 minutes, flip patties, place cheese on top, and cook for another 5 minutes, or until cooked.
6. For the last minute, place a lid on the frying pan (to melt the cheese).
7. Place each patty in an open lettuce leaf, then layer with tomato, avocado, pickles and onion.
8. Serve with dressing on the side.

Horseradish dressing

125 g sour cream

2 tbsp fresh dill

2 tbsp bottled horseradish

1/8 tsp salt

1. Combine all ingredients in a small bowl and mix well.
2. If the sour cream is very thick, then add a little milk or water until the desired consistency is obtained.

NOTE: Any variations of toppings or sauces can be used, but this is my favourite.

BURRITOS

Preparation time: 15 minutes

Serves: 4

Lettuce leaves

600 g beef mince

1 bottle organic spicy pasta sauce
(no sugar in the ingredients)

2 tomatoes, diced

1 cup organic cheese, grated (optional)

1 red onion, finely diced

1 bottle organic salsa
(no sugar in the ingredients)

Guacamole (page 92)

1 tub organic sour cream or yoghurt

1. Brown the mince in a large frying pan, and add the pasta sauce.
2. Simmer on a low heat while preparing the remaining ingredients.
3. Place all the ingredients into individual bowls and serve. Everyone can then put together their own burrito.

Most of us are willing to set out upon the journey of life in the most genious, and most delicate machine ever made—our body—with no more knowledge of its structure than can be gained from gazing in the looking-glass; or of its needs, than a preference for filling up its fuel tank three times a day. More knowledge than this is often regarded as both unnecessary and unpleasant. Yet there are few things more important, more vital to our health, our happiness, and our success in life, than to know how to steer and how to road-repair our body.

DR WOODS HUTCHINSON, A HANDBOOK OF HEALTH

SPANISH QUICHE

Preparation time: 20 minutes

Baking time: 20 minutes

One of the best-kept secrets for radiant skin is eating fat. That's right. One of the most hated substances actually keeps us looking younger, and helps us feel energised. Fats provide energy and are essential for cell rejuvenation and hormone production. They also help us assimilate vitamins A, D, E, and K, so serving vegetables with butter is a perfect combination. Fat is also essential in converting carotene to vitamin A, and is vital for many other processes within a healthy body.

2 potatoes, peeled and chopped

1 onion, diced

2 shallots, sliced

1 red capsicum, diced

2 tomatoes, chopped

9 eggs

1 cup yoghurt

100 g gouda cheese, grated

1 tsp cumin seeds

¼ tsp paprika

1. Preheat the oven to 130°C (150°C if the oven is not fan forced).
2. Fry onion, shallots, capsicum, and potato in a little butter until onions are softened.
3. Mix the eggs and the yoghurt until well combined.
4. Add the onion mixture and the remaining ingredients.
5. Bake in small individual baking dishes for around 20 minutes, or until golden on top. It can also be baked as one large dish for around 40 minutes.

SWEET POTATO SLICE

Preparation time: 15 minutes

Baking time: 40 minutes

Serves: 4

No one can support life without protein in some form. This is because proteins alone contain sufficient amounts of the great element called nitrogen, which forms a large part of every portion of our bodies. This is why they are called proteins, meaning "first foods," or most necessary foods. Whatever we may live on in later life, we all began on a diet of liquid meat (milk), and could have survived and grown up on nothing else.

DR WOODS HUTCHINSON, A HANDBOOK OF HEALTH

1 large sweet potato, peeled

9 eggs

250 g feta cheese, crumbled

2 tbsp fresh dill (or 2 tsp dried)

1 cup yoghurt

1. Preheat oven to 130°C (150°C if the oven is not fan forced).

2. Cut sweet potato into thin slices, and place two layers on the bottom of a large baking dish.

3. Bake in the oven while preparing remaining ingredients (approximately 10 minutes).

4. Beat the eggs in a large bowl. Add the cheese, dill, and yoghurt, and mix thoroughly.

5. Remove the dish with the sweet potato from the oven, and pour the egg mixture on top of the sweet potato.

6. Bake for approximately 40 minutes, or until the egg mixture is firm and cooked. The top will brown slightly.

SALAD WITH GRAPEFRUIT

Preparation time: 10 minutes

Serves: 4

2 cups salad greens (baby spinach, mixed lettuces, or rocket)

1 avocado, chopped

Handful sprouts (optional)

1 pink grapefruit

4 eggs

1. Hard boil the eggs (cover them with water, bring to the boil, and remove from heat after 8 minutes).

2. Peel the grapefruit, remove the white pith (it is very sour), and slice into small slices.

3. Arrange the salad greens, avocado, and grapefruit.

4. Slice the eggs in half, and place on top.

A study has shown that boys born to mothers who experience post-partum depression later display behavioural problems in school. Inhibited emotional development, caused by Mum's post-pregnancy blues is the accepted explanation. Much more likely is the fact that the same deficiencies that cause new mothers to be depressed also inhibit full development of the nervous system in their infants. The solution is proper prenatal nutrition, including plenty of foods rich in nutrients that feed the nervous system, such as eggs, shellfish, fish eggs, liver, cod liver oil, butter and cream.

SALLY FALLON, NOURISHING TRADITIONS

ROAST VEGETABLE SALAD

Preparation time: 15 minutes

Baking time: 30 minutes

Serves: 4

Many people are reluctant to eat bacon, and if they do, they carefully eat it without the fat. The fat is where the fun is. Bacon is one of those small pleasures of life that you can feel free to enjoy. The saturated fat will give you plenty of energy and make you feel great. Make sure your bacon comes from an organic butcher and is nitrate-free.

500 g nitrate-free bacon, chopped

2 cups baby spinach, rocket, or other greens

¼ pumpkin, chopped

1 red or orange capsicum, sliced

1 beetroots, peeled and chopped

1 swede (rutabaga), peeled and chopped

1 avocado, sliced

Extra-virgin olive oil

Salt and pepper (coarse ground black pepper)

1. Preheat oven to 140°C.
2. Place each vegetable in a separate roasting dish.
3. Splash with the olive oil, season with salt and pepper, and mix well with your fingers until the vegetables are well coated.
4. Cook until each vegetable is soft (approximately half an hour; swedes and beetroot take longer, capsicum takes less).
5. Fry the bacon until crispy.
6. Arrange the salad greens on the bottom of the plate, add the vegetables and avocado, and top with bacon.

CHICKEN SALAD

Preparation time: 10 minutes

Serves: 4

TIP: Any salad vegetables with a variety in colour can be used.

Leave your drugs in the chemist's pot if you can heal the patient with food.

HIPPOCRATES

Crumbed chicken breast or thigh (page 96) (easiest with leftovers)

½ cup baby spinach

1 Lebanese cucumber

½ punnet cherry tomatoes

½ red capsicum

1 avocado

1. Arrange the vegetables on the plate, with the baby spinach on the bottom.

2. Cut the chicken breast or thigh into slices, starting from the narrow end. It is easiest to cut the pieces at an angle, following the bone.

3. Arrange the chicken breast on top of the salad vegetables.

CAULIFLOWER RICE SALAD

Preparation time: 20 minutes

Serves: 4

Cauliflower rice is incredibly easy to make and can be used in all sorts of recipes; as the main feature or as a great accompaniment. And, it can be jazzed up with all kinds of fun ingredients. It can be used in stir fries, as fried rice, pilaf, or as just plain rice to soak up rich sauces.

600 g cauliflower (around half a head)

2 tbsp butter

150 g organic, nitrate-free ham, chopped

1 red capsicum, diced

1 Lebanese cucumber, diced

1 red onion, diced

1 cob of corn (steamed and then the kernels cut off) (optional)

½ cup French dressing (page 90)

1. Break the cauliflower into large pieces, place in a food processor, and process using quick pulses until the cauliflower resembles large grains of rice.

2. Melt the butter in a frying pan and add the cauliflower. Toss well until the butter is mixed through, cook for 5 or 6 minutes until cauliflower is cooked (stirring continuously).

3. Place in the fridge to cool while the remaining ingredients are combined in a large bowl.

4. Add the cauliflower rice, stir well, and serve.

Many people think yeast is a women's issue, but men are just as susceptible to Candida. When yeasts, fungi, parasites, or bacteria are present in the body, its immune system and natural defences become compromised. The body eventually breaks down and is overtaken by the organisms within it... It is interesting to note that almost all major diseases—from cancer to AIDS, multiple sclerosis, chronic fatigue syndrome, and Alzheimer's disease—have Candida albicans as part of their symptom profiles. One look at advertising will let you know that the prevalence of Candida albicans has grown to epidemic proportions. Note all the television commercials for products targeting toenail fungus, psoriasis, eczema, dandruff, rectal itching, vaginal yeast infections, bladder frequency, or even memory function... Topical skin preparations are only a temporary solution, as Candida needs to be eradicated internally... Sugary things, including starch and alcohol, feed the yeast.

CAROLINE SUTHERLAND, THE BODY KNOWS HOW TO STAY YOUNG

POTATO SALAD

Preparation time: 25 minutes

Serves: 8

1 kg potatoes, scrubbed and cut into small squares

6 eggs, boiled and peeled

1 small red onion, finely diced

1 cup mayonnaise (page 90)

½ cup gherkin relish (page 92)

1½ tsp course ground black pepper

1 tsp salt

1. Steam potato until soft (approximately 15 minutes), and rinse to remove any waxiness.
2. Set aside to cool. The mayonnaise can be made while the potatoes cool.
3. Place the potatoes in a large bowl.
4. Cut the egg into small squares (use an egg slicer if you have one).
5. Add the mayonnaise, gherkin relish, onion, salt, and pepper and mix until combined well.
6. Place the salad in the refrigerator for 4 hours or overnight. The salad can be served right away, but the taste always improves after a few hours.

I have never been able to find a healthy bottled mayonnaise. Most are full of canola oil and additives. But, mayonnaise is very simple to make.

Similarly, other condiments are equally troubling. Most bottled salad dressings, relishes, or other condiments are full of sugar, unhealthy vegetable oils, and additives, even in the organic grocery store. Quality dressings and other condiments are very easy to make at home.

CONDIMENTS

DRESSINGS

Mayonnaise

Preparation time: 10 minutes

6 egg yolks
1 tbsp Dijon mustard (optional)
100 ml extra-virgin olive oil
½ lemon, juiced
Salt and pepper

1. Place the eggs yolks and mustard in a food processor and process.

2. Continue running the processor, while adding the oil in a very slow trickle.

3. While the processor is still running, add lemon juice, salt, and pepper.

4. Store in an airtight container in the fridge. The mayonnaise will keep for 2 or 3 weeks.

TIP: The left-over egg whites can be added to the sweet potato slice (page 76) in addition to the eggs in the recipe, which will make the slice fluffy. Or, they can be used in place of eggs in the apricot and coconut cookies (page 158).

Greek salad dressing

Preparation time: 5 minutes

¼ cup extra-virgin olive oil
Juice of 1 lemon
½ tbsp fresh oregano or ½ tsp dried
Salt
Coarse ground black pepper

1. Combine lemon, oregano, salt, and pepper.

2. Whisk while slowly adding the oil until the mixture is emulsified (combining two liquids together that don't normally mix easily).

French dressing

Preparation time: 5 minutes

½ cup extra-virgin olive oil
3 tbsp apple cider vinegar
2 tbsp Dijon mustard
½ tsp salt

1. Combine all the ingredients.

2. Whisk with a fork until thoroughly combined.

RELISHES

Guacamole

Preparation time: 5 minutes

2 ripe avocados
1 clove garlic, minced
1 spring onion, finely sliced
1 tomato, finely diced
1 lemon or lime

1. Cut the avocado in half, remove the pip, and peel.
2. Squeeze the lemon or lime juice over the avocado.
3. Mash the avocado with a fork until smooth.
4. Mix the remaining ingredients through and serve.

Gherkin relish

Preparation time: 10 minutes

I cup diced gherkins or cornichons (check that the bottle has no additives)
2 tbsp mustard
3 tbsp filtered water
1½ tsp arrowroot or kuzu
1 tbsp raw honey

1. Chop gherkins in a food processor, until finely diced.
2. Place diced gherkins in a saucepan, add mustard and water, and heat gently.
3. Mix the arrowroot with a small amount of filtered water (approx 2 tsp), and add to the gherkin mixture.
4. Mix thoroughly as the mixture thickens.
5. Once thick, remove from the heat and allow it to cool.
6. Add the honey, and mix well.

When Adelle Davis, the famous nutrition writer, appeared on the Johnny Carson show, she was asked to give a "rule of thumb" for healthy eating. She said, "If it is advertised in the media, don't buy it." An excellent rule indeed. Unfortunately the TV station blipped her out. Viewers never heard the comment. When money goes into advertising, cuts must be made elsewhere so the cheapest ingredients are used—hydrogenated vegetable oils, high fructose corn syrup, white flour and additives that mimic the taste of properly prepared whole food.

SALLY FALLON, NOURISHING TRADITIONS

Gherkin
Relish

Guacamole

Protein is a must for cell regeneration. Our bodies are unable to store protein, so it must be a regular part of the diet. If we don't eat enough protein on a daily basis, the body leeches protein from within itself, which causes muscle loss.

To keep yourself young and vibrant, ensure you eat a good first-class protein three times a day (eggs, meat, or poultry). Fish is also a first-class protein, but because of heavy metals and other contaminants, it is better kept for special occasions.

CRUMBED CHICKEN

Preparation time: 15 minutes

Baking time: 30 minutes

Serves: 4

1½ kg of chicken thighs (or a whole chicken cut into pieces)

²/₃ cup coconut flour

1 tbsp paprika

½ tsp pepper

1 tsp salt

70 g coconut oil and melted butter (½ each)

1. Preheat oven to 160°C (180°C if the oven is not fan forced).
2. Mix dry ingredients on a large plate.
3. Coat each piece of chicken in the crumb mixture and place in a baking dish.
4. Brush with a generous amount of oil (use a dabbing motion rather than a brushing motion; otherwise, the crumbs will come off the chicken).
5. Cook for approximately 30 minutes, or until lightly browned and juice comes out clear when poked with a skewer.

Based on information [supplied by the mainstream health industry], most people naturally think of cholesterol as something damaging, something to be avoided. But cholesterol is absolutely essential for life. It is not some alien chemical that we can remove from our diets, or our bodies...I sometimes remark to those who think my ideas on heart disease are entirely batty, "Why do you think that an egg yolk is full of cholesterol?" Because it takes one hell of a lot of cholesterol to build a healthy chicken. It also takes a hell of a lot of cholesterol to build, and maintain, a healthy human being. In fact, cholesterol is so vital that all cells, apart from neurones, can manufacture cholesterol, and one of the key functions of the liver is to synthesize cholesterol. We also have an entire transportation system dedicated to moving cholesterol around the body.

DR MALCOLM KENDRICK, THE GREAT CHOLESTEROL CON

ROAST PORK WITH CRACKLING

Preparation time: 5 minutes

Baking time: 2 hours

Serves: 4 to 6

> Every single one of the seven countries with the lowest saturated fat consumption has significantly higher rates of heart disease than every single one of the seven countries with the highest saturated fat consumption.
>
> **DR MALCOLM KENDRICK, THE GREAT CHOLESTEROL CON**

Pork roast with a good coverage of fat and rind (approximately 2 kg)

Salt

3 tbsp duck fat

1. Preheat oven to 210°C (20°C hotter on temperatures if oven is not fan forced).

2. Bring pork to room temperature.

3. If the rind hasn't been scored, score it with a sharp knife. My butcher always does this for me, which is the easiest way to do it.

4. Place the meat into a large baking dish and pat dry with a paper towel. Removing all moisture will help the skin crackle.

5. Cover the rind with a good layer of salt.

6. Rub the duck fat into the rind (with the salt).

7. Ensure the oven has reached 210°C, and place the roast in the oven.

8. After 20 minutes, reduce the heat to 170°C.

9. Cook until crackling is golden brown, and the meat is cooked, but still slightly pink in the middle (approximately 2 hours).

SLOW-COOKED LAMB

Preparation time: 5 minutes

Baking time: 3 hours

Serves: 4 to 6

Women often eat less protein than men do, especially because they generally try harder to stay healthy. Because information supplied by the mainstream health industry warns against too much protein, women are more likely to be vegetarian, or significantly reduce meat and fat in their diet. As a result, women often look older than men of a similar age. Because our bodies are made from protein, it is essential to keep our cells regenerating and working effectively. A lack of quality protein from eggs, meat, or poultry causes swelling in the face, wrinkles, and sagging of the jowls and eye-lids. This doesn't just happen to women in their forties or older. These symptoms are now apparent in many women in their twenties.

Leg of lamb, boned

3 tbsp extra-virgin olive oil

3 cloves garlic

1 tbsp fresh oregano (or 1 tsp dried)

Salt

Ground pepper

1 lime or lemon, juiced

1. Preheat oven to 100°C (120°C if oven is not fan forced).
2. Place the lamb in a large baking dish (with a lid), and place 3 cm of filtered water in the bottom.
3. Cover the lamb in the oil, garlic, oregano, salt, pepper, and lime juice.
4. Place the lid on the baking dish, and place in the oven.
5. Baste the lamb with the pan juices every hour.
6. Cook for approximately 3 hours.

ROAST DUCK

Preparation time: 5 minutes

Baking time: 1.5 hours

Serves: 4

Duck meat is extremely nutrient dense, yet it is often described as one of the "worst" meats because it is so fatty. But, I think this attribute makes it one of the best! Not only is the fat good for us, duck is so full of flavour. And we finally have permission to indulge in the juicy, crispy skin. The foods that most of us have spent life-times avoiding are now back on the menu.

Large free range duck

1. Preheat oven to 190°C (210°C if oven is not fan forced).
2. Place the duck in a baking dish (on a rack).
3. Pat dry with a paper towel (removing the moisture helps crisp the skin).
4. Place in the oven.
5. After 20 minutes, reduce the heat to 150°C (170°C if oven is not fan forced).
6. Cook for another hour and 10 minutes, or until juice runs clear.

BUTTER CHICKEN WITH SPICED CAULIFLOWER RICE

Preparation time: 30 minutes

Serves: 4 to 6

Spiced cauliflower rice

1 small cauliflower (around 900 g)

1 tsp cumin seeds

½ tsp tumeric

¼ cup chopped almonds (or slivered almonds)

⅛ cup sultanas (optional)

3 tbsp butter

1. Break the cauliflower into large pieces, process in a food processor using quick pulses until the cauliflower resembles rice.

2. Melt the butter in a frying pan, add the cumin and tumeric, and stir for a minute.

3. Add the cauliflower, mix until the butter and spices are combined, and cook for 6 minutes (stirring continuously).

4. Add the almonds and sultanas, mix, and serve.

8 chicken thighs (preferably with the skin on), cut into fairly large pieces

2 bottles or cans of diced tomato (350 or 400 g)

1 tbsp fresh ginger, finely grated

6 cloves garlic, minced

1 small mild chilli, finely chopped (or a pinch of dried)

½ tsp cinnamon

2 tsp garam masala

Salt to taste

Dash of ground cardamom

200 g butter

100 ml cream

6 tbsp coriander, finely chopped

1. Puree the tomatoes with the spices and salt in a food processor.

2. Brown the chicken pieces in a little butter.

3. Add the tomato mixture to the chicken and simmer for around 10 minutes or until chicken is cooked through.

4. Remove from heat, add the butter, stir and allow to melt.

5. Add the cream and coriander and mix until well combined.

LAMB SHANKS

Preparation time: 10 minutes

Cooking time: 3 hours

Serves: 4

NOTE: I always make my shanks in the early afternoon, and leave them simmering until dinner time. They can cook in three hours, but are tender if they are cooked longer.

4 lamb shanks

1 onion

3 cloves garlic, crushed

2 cans diced tomatoes (approximately 400g each)

2 tbsp fresh rosemary

5 cups chicken stock (page 130), or filtered water

When eating meat, most people trim off the fat, thinking it is dangerous to their health and will make them fat. We always ask our butcher for the fattiest cuts of meat (steaks, roasts, chops, etc). Not only is it tasty, it is essential for good nutrition.

1. In a large cooking pot, sauté the onion and garlic in a tbsp butter until the onion is transparent

2. Add the lamb shanks, and brown slightly.

3. Add the tomatoes, rosemary, and stock.

4. Bring to the boil, and turn down to a low simmer.

5. Simmer between 3 and 6 hours.

ROAST VEGETABLE MOUSSAKA

Preparation time: 1 hour

Baking time: 30 minutes

Serves: 4 to 6

500 g beef mince

1 kg ripe tomatoes, chopped

2 onions, roughly chopped

4 cloves garlic, crushed

1 tbsp oregano (or 1 tsp dried)

1 tbsp basil (or 1 tsp dried)

2 bay leaves

2 cups filtered water

Salt and pepper

Extra-virgin olive oil

1 large eggplant, sliced
(1 cm thick)

2 large sweet potatoes, sliced
(1 cm thick)

4 large zucchini, sliced
(1 cm thick)

NOTE: This meal isn't quick, but it is a lovely meal for a special occasion.

1. Preheat oven to 150°C (170°C if oven is not fan forced).

2. Sprinkle eggplant with salt. Leave for 30 minutes, and rinse and dry.

3. Place tomatoes, onions, and garlic in a baking dish, sprinkle with olive oil, and bake for approximately 30 minutes, or until the vegetables start to caramelise (brown slightly).

4. Place the tomatoes, onions, and garlic in a saucepan, add the herbs and water, and simmer for 30 minutes.

5. Drizzle olive oil over the eggplant, sweet potatoes, and zucchini, and bake for approximately 20 minutes (while the sauce is simmering).

6. Place the sauce in a food processor and blend until smooth.

7. Brown the mince in a skillet, add half of the sauce, and mix.

8. In a large baking dish, layer the bottom with sweet potato. Cover the sweet potato with a thin layer of mince mixture, followed by a layer of eggplant, mince, and then zucchini.

9. Bake for approximately 30 minutes.

10. Serve with the extra tomato sauce.

LAMB CUTLETS WITH SWEET POTATO MASH

Preparation time: 10 minutes

Serves: 4

Lamb is a source of a fat soluble amino acid called Carnitine. Carnitine is essential for energy use and is often used as a supplement to treat congestive heart failure and high triglycerides. It is also excellent for recovery after a heart attack. Lamb, like grass-fed beef, provides a vital source of zinc, magnesium, and selenium, as well as several B vitamins. They are also rich sources of Glutathione. Lamb fat too contains rich levels of palmitoleic acid. This is very active against a variety of pathogenic organisms, particularly those that can colonise our digestive tracts. Eat your lamb with the fat to benefit from this.

ERIC DAVIS, NUTRITION DIAGNOSTICS, BACK TO COOKING BASICS

600 g lamb cutlets (not Frenched)

2 sweet potatoes

Butter

1. Start cooking the sweet potato mash, while preparing the lamb.

2. Heat a large frying pan to medium heat.

3. Cook the lamb cutlets approx 3 minutes on each side.

4. After turning the cutlets the first time, mash the sweet potato with a generous amount of butter and place on each plate.

5. Serve the lamb with the sweet potato and freshly cooked vegetables.

MEAT BALLS WITH BACON

Preparation time: 20 minutes

Cooking time: 15 minutes

Serves: 4

Sauce

1 onion, chopped

3 cloves garlic, crushed

1 cup chicken stock

Salt and pepper to taste

2 cans of diced tomatoes (approx 400 g each)

Meat balls

500 g mince

150 g bacon, diced

1 large egg

Salt and pepper to taste

1 tbsp fresh basil (or 1 tsp dried)

1. Sauté the onion and garlic until the onion is transparent. Add the tomatoes, stock, salt, and pepper. Simmer while preparing the meat balls.

2. In a large bowl, using your hands, mix all the meat ball ingredients. You can use kitchen gloves to protect your hands from the cold.

3. Take spoonfuls of mixture, and roll between your hands to make meat balls approximately 3 cm in diameter.

4. Heat a large frying pan to medium heat and add approximately 1 tbsp coconut oil.

5. Cook the meat balls, turning after approximately 5 minutes, or when browned on one side.

6. After the meat balls are browned on all sides, add them to the sauce, and continue to simmer for 15 minutes.

TIPS: For a quick meal, replace the sauce with quality pasta sauce from the health food store (with no sugar). Basil and garlic sauce works well with this recipe.

CHICKEN PIE WITH BUTTERY MASH

Preparation time: 15 minutes

Baking time: 30 minutes

Serves: 4

Arrowroot flour, the only starch with a calcium ash, is a nutritious food, obtained from the fleshy root stock of a tropical American plant. It is easily digested, well fitted for infants and the convalescent. It resembles cornstarch in being white, fine and powdery. When heated in water in certain portions, it thickens to form a jelly, an excellent thickening agent...The calcium chloride, in the form of calcium found in arrowroot starch, is very important for the maintenance of the proper acid and alkali balances in the human body.

SALLY FALLON, NOURISHING TRADITIONS

4 large potatoes

4 cups chicken, either browned or leftover

4 cups vegetables (such as cabbage or carrots), chopped

4 to 5 tbsp arrowroot or kudzu (mixed with a little water)

2 cups chicken stock (p 126)

150 g butter

Salt

1. Preheat oven to 150°C (170° if oven is not fan forced).
2. Clean potatoes, cut into cubes, and steam.
3. Melt a little of the butter in a frying pan, add vegetables and chicken and mix.
4. Add chicken stock and salt and cook until mixture is simmering.
5. Add the arrowroot or kudzu, and stir well until thickened. Add more if needed.
6. Place the chicken and vegetable mixture into a baking dish.
7. Mash the potatoes with the butter, place on top of the chicken mixture, spread out with a fork, then cook for around 20 minutes or until golden brown.

STIR FRY WITH EGG NOODLES

Preparation time: 10 minutes

Serves: 4

Not eating enough protein causes our faces to lose definition. The face loses its cheekbones and jaw line, and the skin begins to sag, causing it to look older. In addition, eating sugar, starch, and other poor quality carbohydrates causes inflammation in the body, which reduces the amount of collagen in the skin and the body. As a result, wrinkles start to form and muscles start to droop and lose their tone. This is all preventable, and even reversible, by eating a good, healthy diet with plenty of quality protein.

2 cups of mixed vegetables, chopped

2 tbsp butter

¼ cup chicken stock (page 130) or filtered water

2 tbsp tamari

Eggs, lightly beaten (2 per person)

1. Melt 1 tbsp of the butter in a wok or frying pan.
2. Add vegetables, and toss for approximately one minute.
3. Add stock, and cover for approximately 4 minutes, or until vegetables are cooked al denté (cooked, but not soft and overdone).
4. Remove from heat, and add 1 tbsp of the tamari.
5. Melt the other tbsp of butter in a separate frying pan, add the eggs, 2 at a time, and cook until the egg is solid. It is easiest to cook the bottom of the egg in the frying pan, and then put the pan under the grill for a few minutes to finish cooking the top.
6. Roll the egg into logs, then cut into strips. Curl each strip with a chopstick.
7. Add the egg noodles to the vegetables and serve.

FRIED CAULIFLOWER RICE

Preparation time: 20 minutes

Serves: 4

You don't have to cook fancy or complicated masterpieces — just good food from fresh ingredients.

JULIA CHILD

600 g cauliflower (around half a head)

150 g organic bacon (nitrate-free)

2 cups vegetables, chopped into small pieces (such as red capsicum, broccoli, or carrot)

2 shallots, finely chopped

1 tbsp tamari

2 to 3 tbsp butter

1. Break the cauliflower into large pieces, place into a food processor, and process using quick pulses until the cauliflower resembles rice.

2. Fry bacon in a wok or a large frying pan.

3. Once bacon is cooked, add vegetables, and sauté in the bacon fat for approximately 3 minutes.

4. Add the cauliflower, and stir well until all the cauliflower is shiny.

5. Cook for a further 5 or 6 minutes, stirring continuously, until cauliflower is cooked.

6. Add the shallots, toss through, and cook for a further minute.

7. Remove from the heat, add the tamari and butter, and mix thoroughly.

CHICKEN CURRY

Preparation time: 10 minutes

Serves: 4

Turmeric is a super spice. It has strong anti-inflammatory properties and has been proven to prevent neurological diseases like Alzheimer's. Turmeric also helps us detoxify by removing toxins and carcinogens from our system. Anything that reduces inflammation will keep us looking younger and more vibrant.

1 onion, chopped

1 tbsp butter

1 tbsp curry powder (quality powder from Indian or organic grocery store)

1 can of coconut cream (quality from organic grocery store with no additives)

1 cup chicken stock (page 130)

1 cup cooked chicken (or any kind of leftover meat)

2 cups of mixed vegetables, chopped

1. Sauté onion in butter until transparent.
2. Add curry powder, stir for a minute.
3. Add the coconut cream and stock.
4. Let the mixture simmer and reduce (approximately ½ hour).
5. Add the vegetables and chicken, cover, and continue to cook until the vegetables are cooked al denté (cooked, but not soft and overdone).

IRISH STEW

Preparation time: 10 minutes

Cooking time: 3 hours

Serves: 4

1½ kg lamb chops, chopped

500 g bacon, nitrate-free

4 potatoes, chopped

5 large carrots, sliced

1 tbsp fresh thyme (1 tsp dried)

6 cups stock (page 130)

1. In a large pot, fry the bacon.
2. Add the lamb and brown the chops slightly.
3. Add the stock, and simmer for 2 to 3 hours.
4. Add the vegetables, and simmer for another half an hour.

TIP: Have the butcher chop the lamb.

In 1988, the Surgeon General's office decided to gather together all the evidence linking saturated fat to heart disease, and thus silence any remaining naysayers forever. Eleven years later, the project was killed. In a letter circulated it was stated that the office "did not anticipate fully the magnitude of the additional expertise and staff resources that would be needed." After eleven years, they needed additional expertise and staff resources? What had they been doing up to then?...Bill Harlan of the oversight Committee and Associate Director of the office of Disease Prevention at the NIH, commented: "The report was initiated with a preconceived opinion of the conclusions, but the science behind those opinions was clearly not holding up. Clearly the thoughts of yesterday were not going to serve us very well." I shall do a translation: "We were wrong, the idea that saturated fat causes heart disease was wrong. Everything we always thought about the idea is wrong. Full stop."

DR MALCOLM KENDRICK, THE GREAT CHOLESTEROL CON

BEEF STEW

Preparation time: 10 minutes

Cooking time: 3½ hours

Serves: 4 to 6

TIP: Ask the butcher to chop the beef.

Myth: Heart disease in America is caused by consumption of cholesterol and saturated fat from animal products.

Truth: During the period of rapid increase in heart disease (1920–1960), American consumption of animal fats declined but consumption of hydrogenated and industrially processed vegetable oils increased dramatically.

USDA-HNI

1½ kg stewing beef, chopped

1 onion, chopped

4 cups beef or chicken stock (page 130)

2 cans diced tomatoes (approx 400g)

1 tbsp fresh oregano (1 tsp dried)

4 cups stewing vegetables (such as sweet potato, potato, carrot)

1½ tbsp kuzu or arrowroot, dissolved in a little water (optional)

Salt and pepper

Butter for frying and serving

1. Melt butter in a large pot, add onion, and cook until it is transparent.
2. Add the meat, and cook until it is browned (stirring frequently).
3. Add the stock, tomatoes, and oregano.
4. Simmer for 3 hours, and add the vegetables.
5. Simmer for another 30 minutes, or until vegetables are tender.
6. To thicken, add the kuzu or arrowroot and stir well.
7. Add a dab of butter to each serve.

PEA AND HAM SOUP

Preparation time: 10 minutes

Cooking time: 4 hours

Serves: 4 to 6

Please understand my friend, that where you find yourself tomorrow is a function of the positive decisions and actions you take today.

**AKIN A. AWOLAJA,
EDUCATOR OF WISE LIVING**

1 ham hock (organic, nitrate free)

500 g green split peas

Filtered water

1. Soak the peas in filtered water overnight in a large saucepan.

2. Rinse the peas, add 8 cups of filtered water, and bring to the boil.

3. Add the ham hock, and reduce to a simmer.

4. After simmering for an hour or so, remove the ham hock, let it cool slightly, then remove the meat from the bone (using gloves), and chop into small pieces.

5. Return the meat to the saucepan, and continue simmering until peas are soft (approximately 4 hours in total). After the peas start to soften and sink to the bottom, stir frequently to avoid the peas sticking and burning.

PUMPKIN SOUP

Preparation time: 20 minutes

Serves: 4 to 6

1 kg pumpkin, chopped and peeled

2 cups chicken stock (page 130)

Salt and pepper

1. Steam the pumpkin until soft (approximately 10 minutes).

2. Place the pumpkin in a food processor, and process until smooth.

3. Add the stock, salt, and pepper, and process until smooth.

NOTE: The soup can be served with a dollop of sour cream or yoghurt.

Quality food can be expensive, which deters a lot of people from buying it. However, if you knew just how much money you would save on future doctors' bills, hospital bills, and physiotherapy bills (from joint and tissue breakdown), you would no longer see it as an optional expense.

CHICKEN SOUP

Preparation time: 10 minutes

Serves: 4

1 cup cooked chicken
(leftovers from a roast chicken)

4 cups chicken stock

1 carrot, cubed

1 cup mixed vegetables,
chopped and steamed (al denté)

4 eggs, lightly beaten

1. Add the stock, chicken, and carrots to a saucepan and simmer.

2. Slowly add the egg; use a fork to separate once it hits the soup (it will quickly become fluffy as it cooks).

3. Remove the soup from the heat, add the vegetables, and serve.

Chicken stock

Bones, cartilage, and drippings from 2 roast chickens or 5 chicken frames (carcasses) from the organic butcher

10 cups filtered water

¼ cup apple cider vinegar

1. In a large cooking pot, add all the ingredients, and simmer for 12 to 24 hours.

2. Before you go to bed, check to ensure it has enough water and won't cook dry.

Cholesterol is formed in our bodies from carbohydrate chains, not fat. The cholesterol that we eat from animal fat is metabolised by the body, and we don't absorb any other. What our doctors measure is the cholesterol we've manufactured, regardless of fat intake. In other words, if we eat a high cholesterol food, that cholesterol won't become part of our system... Cholesterol is a vitally important component in the hormone-balance equation. With the very best intentions, many people greatly reduce fats in the diet and often affect critical hormone function in the process...Fats from animal and vegetable sources form necessary building blocks for cell membranes and a variety of hormone processes.

CAROLINE SUTHERLAND, THE BODY KNOWS HOW TO STAY YOUNG

Plant-based foods add colour and variety to a LCHF diet. I never serve flavourless steamed vegetables; they are always braised with melted butter or served with tamari (a beautiful traditional soy sauce) or fresh herbs.

Try and purchase different types of vegetables; choose different colours and varieties. For example, try spinach, kale, broccoli, Brussels sprouts, cabbage, snow peas, zucchini, asparagus, squash, green beans, red capsicum, sweet potato, carrot, pumpkin, swedes (rutabaga), cauliflower, eggplant, beetroot, etc. If you see something new that you haven't seen before, try it. Variety in vegetables provides a large array of different antioxidants, vitamins, minerals, and other nutrients.

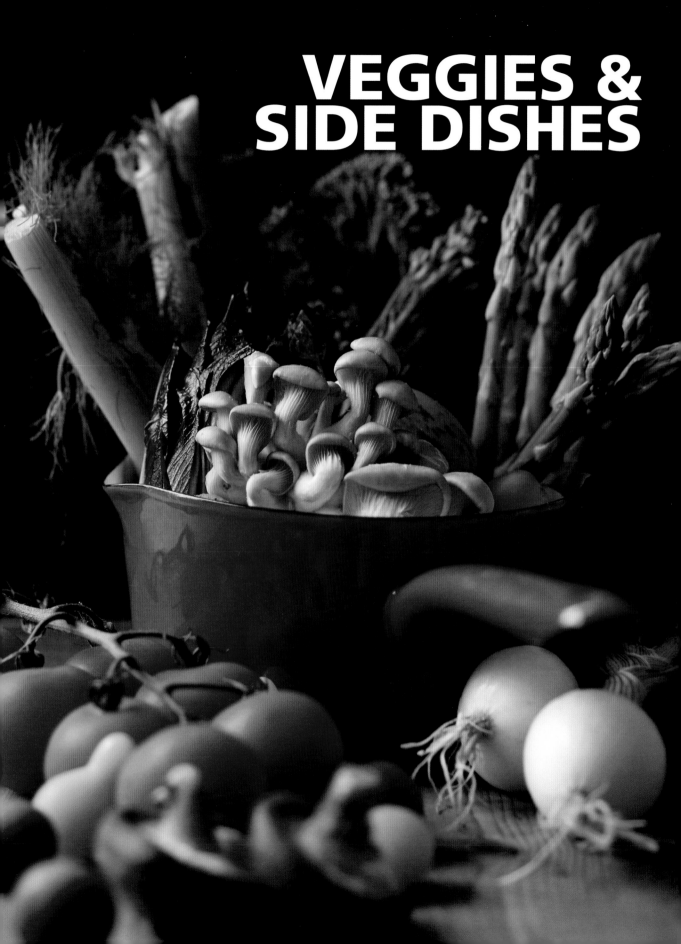

VEGGIES & SIDE DISHES

ARTICHOKE WITH GARLIC BUTTER

Preparation time: 10 minutes

Cooking time: 1 hour

Serves: 4

4 artichokes (or one per person)

¾ cup butter

1 clove garlic, crushed

1. Boil artichokes for 50 minutes. I put my steamer on top of them to ensure they are submerged in the boiling water.

2. Remove, and drain excess water.

3. Put the butter and garlic into a small saucepan, and melt gently.

4. Serve each artichoke with a dish of garlic butter.

NOTE: To eat the artichoke, peel each leaf, place it upside down in your mouth, and pull the soft fleshy part off with your teeth. As you get further into the middle, the soft part will get bigger and bigger. Eventually, the entire leaf will be edible. The middle is the best part: the artichoke heart, which can be eaten whole. For people who have removed the heart from a raw artichoke and had to be cautious with the hairs around the heart, these hairs become soft and edible when the artichoke is boiled.

The French eat more saturated fat than we do in the UK. They smoke more, take less exercise, and have the same cholesterol/LDL levels, the same HDL levels. They also have the same average blood pressure and the same rate of obesity. And you know what? They have one-quarter the rate of heart disease that we do. One-quarter! In fact, the French consume more saturated fat than any other nation in Europe, and they have the lowest rate of heart disease. The only other nation that comes close to their super-low rate of heart disease is Switzerland, and the Swiss have the second highest consumption of saturated fat in Europe.

DR MALCOLM KENDRICK, THE GREAT CHOLESTEROL CON

BAKED POTATO WITH THE WORKS

Preparation time: 5 minutes

Baking time: 45 minutes

Serves: 4

The most useful and wholesome single fat is the one which is in greatest demand—butter. Butter is the best and most wholesome of our common fats because it is most easily digested and most readily absorbed...Plenty of sweet butter is one of the most important and necessary elements in our diet, especially in childhood. And if children are allowed to eat pretty nearly as much as they want of it on their bread or potatoes, and plenty of its liquid form, cream, on their berries and puddings, it will save the necessity of many a dose of cod-liver oil.

DR WOODS HUTCHINSON, A HANDBOOK OF HEALTH

4 large potatoes

Coconut oil

Salt

Toppings (such as butter, chives, shallots, bacon, sour cream, vegetables)

1. Preheat the oven to 140°C (160°C if oven is not fan forced).

2. Wash and dry the potato.

3. Coat the potato with oil and salt, and place in the oven on a rack.

4. Bake for approximately 45 minutes (or until a fork goes through easily).

5. Cut in half, and garnish with your favourite toppings.

CUCUMBER NOODLES

Preparation time: 10 minutes

Serves: 4

TIP: This dish is a light, fresh accompaniment for any kind of meat or egg dish.

Today, many people eat the same foods day in and day out. Different plants provide us with different essential nutrients. By consuming an array of different fruits and veggies, you will get a better variety of nutrients as well as limit your chances of acquiring food intolerances. The deeper its colour, the more antioxidants a fruit or veggie will likely provide.

PAUL CHEK, HOW TO EAT, MOVE, AND BE HEALTHY!

2 large Lebanese cucumbers

1 lime, juiced

1 tbsp sesame seeds

1 tsp of dried dill

1 tsp fresh dill (optional)

1 tsp sesame oil

1. Using a good quality peeler, peel the cucumber to form strips.
2. Add the remaining ingredients, and toss.

GREEK STYLE GREEN BEANS

Preparation time: 15 minutes

Cooking time: 30 minutes

Serves: 4

500 g green beans

1 can diced tomatoes (approx 400 g)

2 onions, chopped

3 cloves garlic, crushed

1 cup extra-virgin olive oil

1 tbsp butter

¼ cup water

Salt and freshly ground pepper

1. In a large pot, sauté the onions in the butter while you remove the tips of the beans.

2. Stir in the garlic and sauté a few minutes more.

3. Add the remaining ingredients.

4. Stir, reduce to a simmer, cover and simmer on low heat for approx 30 minutes (until beans are tender, but still have a shiny green colour to them).

5. If the liquid reduces too much during cooking (so there is a lack of sauce), add more water.

Go ahead and eat those veggies! They help prevent lung cancer, but it isn't just the beta carotene in them that protects you. Over and above beta carotene, not-so-well known vegetable constituents, such as lutein, lycopene, and indoles, could be virtually anonymous soldiers who battle to protect our lungs. Indoles and related substances in vegetables have prevented various tumour formations in animals. In his human study, LeMarchland found that while a diet high in beta carotene reduced risk of lung cancer by three times in females and by two times in males, a diet of many different vegetables reduced the risk by seven times in females and by three times in males. Variety may be the spice of life, or, in the case of vegetables, it could be life itself.

JAMES. F. SCHEER, HEALTH FREEDOM NEWS

BRAISED VEGETABLES WITH DILL

Preparation time: 10 minutes

Serves: 4

TIP: Any vegetables can be used. Using an array of different colours makes the dish more appealing. I toss in a bit of extra melted butter at the end for extra flavour.

2 cups mixed vegetables, chopped (such as Brussels sprouts, cabbage, capsicum, and broccoli)

2 tbsp chicken stock or filtered water

2 tbsp butter

1 tbsp fresh dill

1. Heat the butter in a large frying pan, on medium heat.

2. Add vegetables, and toss for a minute.

3. Add 2 tbsp filtered water or chicken stock.

4. Cover, and simmer for approximately two minutes.

5. Stir, add the dill, and cook for another two minutes, or until the vegetables are cooked al denté (cooked, but not soft and overdone).

Health recommendations to eat more vegetables are normally coupled with the mandate to 'eat less fat.' Vegetables are full of fat soluble vitamins. We aren't able to assimilate those vitamins without fat. As a result, health surveys continually show that many people in Western countries are deficient in vitamins A, D, k_2 and E; all essential nutrients and all fat soluble. Adding butter or bacon to vegetables not only adds taste but makes them far healthier.

Desserts are often the most challenging when we are trying to remove sugar and processed food from our diet. But, natural sweeteners are easy substitutes once we know the right way to use them. And, learning to cook differently means that there is no deprivation. We can still eat chocolate, make cakes for birthday parties, enjoy ice blocks and other little pleasures that make life that much more enjoyable.

And, of course, with full permission to indulge in fats, we can liberally enjoy our butter, whipped cream and other luscious extravagances; without any of the guilt. Enjoy!

HEALTHY DESSERTS

PASSION FRUIT CHEESE CAKE

370 g organic quark,
brought to room temperature

Juice of 6 passion fruits
(strain seeds with strainer)

Juice of an orange

1½ tbsp raw honey

5 sheets gelatine

200 ml organic cream

Preparation time: 10 minutes

Serves: 10 to 12

1. Soak the gelatine in cold filtered water

2. Mix the quark with an electric beater until smooth.

3. Slowly add the passionfruit juice, orange juice, and honey while mixing.

4. Squeeze excess water from the gelatine, place into a small saucepan, and gently heat until dissolved. Add to the mixture, and beat until smooth (the mixture will thicken slightly).

5. Whip the cream, and fold through the mixture.

6. Pour into the crust, and refrigerate for 4 hours, or until firm.

Pie crust

250 g almond meal

3 tbsp butter

Zest of one orange

1 tbsp rice malt syrup

1 egg, lightly whisked

Preparation time: 10 minutes

Baking time: 15 minutes

1. Preheat oven to 100°C.

2. In a mixing bowl, combine almond meal and melted butter. Mix well (using fingers is easiest).

3. Add remaining ingredients, and mix well with a spoon.

4. Place the mixture into a pie tin, and press into a smooth crust using the back of a spoon.

5. Bake in the oven for approximately 10 to 15 minutes or until golden (watch it carefully because it can burn easily).

6. Place the crust into the refrigerator to set.

CHOCOLATE MOUSSE PIE

Preparation time: 20 minutes

Serves: 10 to 12

60 g cacao butter

3 tbsp good quality cacao

4 sheets gelatine (titanium strength)

2 tbsp filtered water

3 eggs, separated

1½ tsp vanilla extract (page 166)

2½ tbsp raw honey

200 ml organic, pure cream

Pie crust (page 146)

1. Soak the gelatine in cold water.

2. In a saucepan, on a very gentle heat, melt the cacao butter, and add the cacao, vanilla, and filtered water.

3. Remove from heat, add the softened gelatine, and whisk until completely dissolved.

4. Add the egg yolks, and whisk until thickened and smooth.

5. Set aside to cool.

6. Whip the cream, and set aside.

7. In a separate bowl, beat the egg whites until they have stiff peaks.

8. Slowly add the honey while beating, and continue until the mixture is glossy.

9. Give the cream a stir to make sure it hasn't fallen any (if it has, just fluff up a little with a whisk).

10. Gently fold the chocolate mixture into the cream.

11. Beat the egg whites again for a minute to make sure they haven't fallen, and gently fold the chocolate mixture into the egg whites.

12. Pour into the pie crust, and chill for 4 hours (or until set).

New evidence points a sharp finger at sugar as a food item that makes us grow older faster! The quick rush of sugar into the bloodstream is probably what does it. In much the same way as a steak turns brown and toughens on the barbeque grill, a reaction between the sugar and protein called the "browning effect"—sugar reacts with protein in human cells—occurs, particularly as human cells age... Ageing seems to be accelerated when the body must cope with excessive sugar and is unable to do it—as in diabetes. [Scientists] now feel that the collagen, which glues our trillions of cells together, is affected by glucose, which acts upon DNA causing mutations in this genetic material that permit the start and the spread of cancer...Any sudden rush of glucose into the blood-stream—from a candy bar, a glass of orange juice, or a couple of teaspoons of granulated sugar in the coffee—stresses the pancreas to produce more insulin. Excessive sugar making the rounds of the bloodstream brings about cross-linking and ageing.

JAMES F. SCHEER HEALTH FREEDOM NEWS

CHOCOLATE CAKE WITH BUTTER CREAM ICING

Preparation time boiling oranges: 1 hour
Prep time cake: 30 minutes
Baking time: 1 hour
Serves: 8 to 12

TIP: You can make one large cake or two smaller ones with an adjusted cooking time of 40 minutes.

2 oranges

6 eggs

1 tsp vanilla extract (page 166)

1 tsp stevia (use pure stevia (check ingredients) or the cake will not be sweet)

3 cups almond meal

1 tbsp baking powder

½ cup raw cacao powder

1 tsp cinnamon

1. Preheat oven to 140°C (160°C if the oven is not fan forced).

2. Butter a cake tin (use a good layer of butter).

3. Boil the oranges in filtered water for one hour.

4. Mix the almond meal, baking powder, and cinnamon and set aside.

5. Cut the oranges into quarters, remove the pith and any seeds, and process in a food processor until very smooth (skin and all).

6. Add the vanilla and stevia to the orange mixture, process again, and set aside.

7. Mix eggs with electric beater until very fluffy with soft peaks (yes, you can get soft peaks with whole eggs, but it takes around 8 to 10 minutes).

8. Mix the cacao into the orange mixture, then add the orange and almond mixtures to the egg, and gently fold them through, maintaining as much air as possible in the egg.

9. Pour into the cake tin, cover with baking paper so the top doesn't get too dark, and bake for approximately one hour, or until a skewer comes out clean.

Icing

375 g unsalted butter, slightly softened

1½ tsp vanilla

2½ tbsp raw honey

2 tbsp cacao powder

1. Whisk butter and honey until smooth.

2. Add the cacao powder and vanilla and continue whisking until light and fluffy.

ORANGE CINNAMON CAKE

Prep time boiling orange: 1 hour

Prep time cake: 30 minutes

Baking time: 1 hour

Serves: 8 to 12

2 oranges

6 eggs

2 tsp vanilla extract (page 166)

1 tsp stevia (use pure stevia (check ingredients) or the cake will not be sweet)

3 cups almond meal

2 tsp cinnamon

1 tbsp baking powder

1. Preheat oven to 140°C (160°C if the oven is not fan forced).

2. Butter a cake tin (use a good layer of butter).

3. Boil the oranges in filtered water for one hour.

4. Mix the almond meal, baking powder, and cinnamon, and set aside.

5. Cut the oranges into quarters, remove the pith and any seeds, and process in a food processor until very smooth (skin and all).

6. Add the vanilla and stevia to the orange mixture, process again, and set aside.

7. Mix eggs with electric beater until very fluffy with soft peaks (yes, you can get soft peaks with whole eggs, but it takes around 8 to 10 minutes).

8. Place the orange and almond mixtures into the egg, and gently fold them through, maintaining as much air as possible in the egg.

9. Pour into the cake tin, cover with baking paper so the top doesn't get too dark, and bake for approximately one hour, or until a skewer comes out clean.

TIP: You can make one large cake or two smaller ones with an adjusted cooking time of 40 minutes.

FRUIT TRIFLE

Assembly time once cake and custard are made: 15 minutes

Serves: 8

Is time an issue? The time you take to better care for your health will save you immeasurable amounts of time later in life when others of a similar age are struggling with illness and disease, and you are living a full, vivacious life.

Orange cake (page 152)

Pouring custard (page 178)

600ml organic pure cream

Punnet strawberries, sliced

2 cups of any other type of fruit, such as nectarines

1. Whip the cream, until fluffy.
2. Arrange trifle glasses on the bench and assemble the trifle in any order, with layers of fruit, cake, custard and cream. Garnish with fruit and cream.

This trifle is a beautiful, extravagant dessert that is easy to make. Make the cake and the custard ahead of time, and allow them to cool before assembling the trifle.

Fruit tea jelly

2 fruit flavoured herbal tea bags

2 cups boiling water

4 sheets gelatine (titanium strength)

.16 g stevia (4 scoops of Nirvana or 9 drops of liquid stevia)

Preparation time: 10 minutes

Serves: 4

1. Place the two tea bags in the water and leave for 5 minutes.

2. Remove the tea bags.

3. Add the stevia and stir.

4. Add the gelatine and stir until completely dissolved.

5. Pour into glasses and place in the refrigerator until set (approximately 3 or 4 hours).

Lime and pear jelly

1 lime, juiced

1 cup boiling water

4 sheets gelatine (titanium strength)

.12 g stevia (3 scoops of Nirvana or 9 drops of liquid stevia)

Small pear, diced

Preparation time: 10 minutes

Serves: 4

1. Place boiling water in a bowl, add gelatine and stir until dissolved.

2. Cool to room temperature (so you don't cook the lime juice).

3. Add enough filtered water to the lime juice to make 1 cup of liquid.

4. Add the lime, stevia and filtered water to the gelatine mixture, and stir.

5. Pour into glasses, add a few pieces of pear to each glass, then place in the refrigerator until set (approximately 3 or 4 hours).

In the treatment of feverish and acute infectious diseases, it is evident that gelatine plays a double role. In the first place, the nutritive qualities of gelatine, its ready absorption and colloidal properties, make it ideally suited for inclusion in the diet both during the height of fever and during convalescence. Bayley emphasised this factor from a nurse's viewpoint, observing that gelatine acts as a base for the preparation of many dainty, pleasing dishes which appeal to the patient with poor appetite, thus providing much-needed nourishment.

N.R. GOTTHOFFER, GELATIN IN NUTRITION AND MEDICINE

Apricot & coconut cookies

Preparation time: 5 minutes
Preparation time: 20 minutes
Serves: 4 to 6

½ cup dried apricots, cut into small chunks

1¼ cup desiccated coconut

3 eggs

1. Preheat oven to 120°C (140°C if the oven is not fan forced).

2. Beat eggs.

3. Add dry ingredients.

4. Roll into small balls, and place on a baking dish.

5. Press each ball with a fork (while holding the outside with your fingers to maintain its structure). Turn the fork in the opposite direction and press the ball again.

6. Bake for approximately 20 minutes, or until golden.

Almond cookies

Preparation time: 15 minutes
Preparation time: 20 minutes
Serves: 4 to 6

2⅛ cups almond meal

50 g butter, room temperature

4 tbsp rice malt syrup

1 egg, beaten

Rind of one orange

½ tsp vanilla extract (page 166)

⅛ cup sultanas

1 tsp baking powder

1. Preheat oven to 120°C (140°C if oven is not fan forced).

2. Butter a baking sheet or large baking dish.

3. In a large bowl, mix the butter and syrup with an electric beater until creamy.

4. Add the egg, and mix well.

5. Add the remaining ingredients and mix until smooth.

6. Roll into small balls, place onto the baking sheet, then gently flatten into cookie shapes.

7. Bake for approximately 20 minutes, or until golden brown.

8. Brush with melted butter and serve.

ANNA'S BUCKWHEAT PANCAKES

This is my daughter Anna's recipe, and it always goes down as a treat!

Unlike other grains, buckwheat is actually related to the rhubarb, and is not actually a grain at all. It is a great substitute for wheat and other grains frequently used in baking. Buckwheat also has a low glycemic index and contains a compound that has been proven to reduce glucose levels in the blood. You can enjoy pasta, muffins, and other baked goods while keeping your blood glucose level within normal range. Buckwheat has also been proven to have anti-inflammatory properties, so is great for keeping us younger.

Preparation time: 20 minutes

Serves: 4

½ cup buckwheat flour

⅛ cup coconut flour

1 tsp baking powder

.16 g stevia (4 scoops of Nirvana or 12 drops of liquid stevia)

1 egg, separated

1 cup of milk

Pinch of salt

Blueberries (optional)

1. Sift the flours and baking powder into a bowl. Add the salt and stevia and make a well in the middle. If using liquid stevia, add it to the egg yolk and milk in the next step instead.

2. Pour the egg yolk and milk in and whisk well until just combined.

3. Beat the egg whites until peaks form and gently fold into the batter.

4. Heat a cast iron or healthy non stick fry pan over medium heat and brush with oil.

5. Drop tablespoons of batter onto the pan. If adding blueberries, gently place a few berries into the top of the pancake. Cook the pancakes until bubbles appear on the top side and then flip it over. Cook for another minute or so until golden.

6. Plain pancakes can be served with butter and honey.

BANANA MUFFINS

Preparation time: 20 minutes

Makes: 18 muffins

Baking time: 30 minutes

TIP: This is a banana bread best eaten with butter. For a sweeter muffin, add more stevia.

Yesterday is history. Tomorrow is a mystery. Today is a gift. That's why it is called the present.

ALICE MORSE EARLE

8 eggs

100 g butter, melted

100 g coconut oil, melted

4 large bananas, mashed

2 apples, grated

½ cup sultanas (optional)

260 g buckwheat flour

2 cups almond meal

3 tsp baking powder

⅛ tsp stevia

1. Preheat oven to 130°C (150°C if the oven is not fan forced).
2. Place paper muffin cases in 2 muffin tins.
3. Mix eggs, butter, oil, and stevia thoroughly.
4. Add apple, banana, and sultanas, and mix well.
5. Mix flour, almond meal, and baking powder, add to the cake mixture, and mix well.
6. Pour into the muffin cases, and bake for approximately 30 minutes or until golden brown and a skewer comes out clean.

FRUIT SALAD WITH WHIPPED CREAM

Preparation time: 5 minutes

Serves: 4

2 apples

½ punnet of strawberries

¼ punnet of blueberries

1 other piece of fruit of choice

200 ml organic pure cream

1. Whip the cream until fluffy.
2. Cut the fruit into small pieces, place into a bowl, and toss.
3. Serve in individual bowls with a dollop of cream.

> When a high GI food is eaten with fat or protein, the blood glucose level stays in a normal range. For example, when a potato is eaten with butter or sour cream and some protein (like meat, or fish), the blood glucose becomes normally elevated. The fat and protein stabilise the starch in the potato, because fat and protein travel slower through the body.
>
> **NANCY APPLETON, PHD, SUICIDE BY SUGAR**

TIP: Any combination of fruit can be used. Apples are always a good basic fruit to start with. When eating fruit, stick mostly to the non-sweet fruits or the fruits that are high in malic acid (which is what gives them their tart taste). Malic acid is extremely beneficial to our health, helps balance our pH, aids digestion, helps absorption of nutrients, and more. Apples are very high in malic acid. Other fruits high in malic acid include berries, kiwi fruit, pineapple, plumbs, and cherries. Lemons and limes are also extremely high in malic acid, but obviously aren't the right choice for a fruit salad, although they taste lovely drizzled on the apple.

Use the sweet fruits such as banana, orange, and mango (especially mango) more sparingly. For example, use one banana in a recipe for four or six people. For those wanting to reduce carbohydrates even further, avoid the sweeter fruits altogether.

VANILLA EXTRACT

The vanilla essence sold in the supermarket is made with artificial vanilla flavour, chemicals, and sugar. Quality vanilla extract can be purchased from health food stores, but is very expensive. However, you can make a beautiful one at home for very little cost. You can use fresh vanilla beans, or save all your used vanilla beans when cooking, and use those instead. Used vanilla beans still have plenty of seeds in them (it is impossible to scrape them all out), so they create a very strong extract.

Preparation time: 5 minutes

2 large vanilla beans

2 cups vodka
(or enough to fill a small bottle)

1. Find a small glass bottle (a used glass 200ml juice bottle is a great size).

2. If using fresh vanilla beans, cut the vanilla beans lengthways from top to bottom so the seeds are exposed.

3. Place vanilla beans inside the bottle, and fill the bottle with vodka.

4. Put a lid on the bottle, and place it in a dark place.

5. Every few days or so, give it a good shake.

6. After a few weeks, it will form a beautiful vanilla extract, which will continue to get stronger as it sits in the cupboard.

If we eat wrongly, no doctor can cure us; if we eat rightly, no doctor is needed.

VICTOR G. ROCINE

DARK CHOCOLATE

Preparation time: 30 minutes

Makes: 6 large blocks

250 g raw cacao butter

250 g raw cacao mass

1 tsp stevia

2 tsp vanilla extract (page 166)

$1/16$ tsp salt

½ cup goji berries or dried cranberries
(1 cup if no nuts are added)

½ cup unsalted cashews or macadamias
(optional)

> **TIP:** A chocolate making kit can be purchased from christinecronau.com/chocolate, including cacao mass, cacao butter, stevia, and vanilla beans. Avoid getting water in the mixture. Temperatures must be exact to make a smooth, glossy chocolate; a thermometer is essential, but it is easier than it looks!

1. Place cacao butter and cacao mass in a bowl placed over a pan of water (or double boiler). Make sure the water does not touch the bowl.

2. Using low heat, melt by heating to at least 45°C, but try to keep it under 55°C.

3. Remove the bowl from the hot water and place into an ice bath (a pie tin or shallow bowl containing water and ice).

4. Add the stevia and vanilla and mix thoroughly with a whisk.

5. Continue mixing while the mixture cools to 27°C.

6. Place the mixture back on the hot water. Very carefully heat to between 30°C and 31°C, but remove from the heat before the temperature reaches 30°C. The temperature will continue to rise a few more degrees. If it doesn't rise enough, keep placing it on and off the heat until it reaches 30°C. If it goes over 32°C, it will have to be tempered again (steps 2 to 6).

7. Cool to 27°C, stirring occasionally. The mixture can go back in the ice bath temporarily to speed this up.

8. Add the berries and nuts and stir.

9. Wipe the water from the bottom of the bowl (to avoid drips in the moulds) and spoon into moulds.

10. Place in the refrigerator until set (the corners are lifting from the mould), remove from the mould, and store in an air tight container.

CHOCOLATE FAT BOMBS

What are fat bombs? Fats, especially natural saturated fats like coconut oil are incredibly nourishing and also help us lose weight. And, a good LCHF diet includes a very high percentage of fat. In fact, when most people find out their ideal fat intake, they are often surprised at how much fat is right for them. Then, they often wonder how to actually consume the amount of fat they need. Fat bombs have become popular in the LCHF world; they are little tasty treats with a concentrated hit of those all-important fats. You can find out your ideal fat intake by becoming a member of my website *christinecronau.com/member*

Preparation time: 10 minutes

Serves: 4 to 6

3 tbsp cacao powder

250 g coconut oil, melted

2 cups desiccated coconut

1/8 tsp stevia

1 tsp raw honey

4 dried apricots, finely diced (optional)

1. Combine cacao powder and coconut oil thoroughly with a whisk.
2. Add the remaining ingredients and mix well.
3. Spoon into mini patty papers and refrigerate until set (approximately 4 hours).

The much-maligned saturated fats—which Americans are trying to avoid—are not the cause of modern diseases. If they were, and if the saturated fat or cholesterol myth were true, none of us would be alive today because saturated fat was the primary energy source for most of our ancestors. Studies of North American Indians, Eskimos, and other tribes suggest that as much as 80% of their daily caloric intake was from fat, most of which was saturated animal fat.

PAUL CHEK, HOW TO EAT, MOVE, AND BE HEALTHY!

APRICOT SLICE

Preparation time: 5 minutes

Serves: 4 to 6

1¼ cup desiccated coconut

¾ cup extra-virgin coconut oil

5 apricots, sliced into tiny pieces

⅛ tsp stevia

1. If the coconut oil is solid because the temperature is cool, melt it on a gentle heat while preparing the dry ingredients.

2. Mix coconut and stevia thoroughly.

3. Add apricots and melted coconut oil and mix well.

4. Cover a flat tray with baking paper, and pour the mixture onto the tray.

5. Spread the mixture out so it is flat.

6. Place in the fridge for approximately an hour, or until set.

7. Cut into squares, place into an airtight container, and store in the fridge.

[Coconut] provides calcium, iron, magnesium, phosphorus, potassium, iodine, and many trace minerals. The coconut contains up to 60 percent fat, and this fat is 92 percent saturated. But this is no reason to avoid coconut products. The principle fatty acid in coconut milk, lauric acid, is a medium-chain 12-carbon saturated fatty acid that has potent antiviral, antifungal and antimicrobial properties. In vitro, it will inactivate the HIV virus as well as the measles virus, herpes simplex virus-1, vesicular stomatitis virus, visna virus and cytomegalovirus. Coconut oil is our best source of lauric acid and is now being used to treat both AIDS and candida because of its antipathogenic affects in the gut. When absorbed, the medium-chain fatty acids in coconut oil give quick energy. The medium-chain fatty acids strengthen the immune system. Coconut oil is a good substitute for hydrogenated oils. Is this why we hear so much adverse publicity about the coconut?

**SALLY FALLON,
NOURISHING TRADITIONS**

BLISS BALLS

Preparation time: 10 minutes

Serves: 4 to 6

1 cup almonds, soaked overnight in lukewarm, filtered water

2 tbsp raw cacao powder

2 bananas

1 tbsp lemon juice

½ cup coconut oil

2 cups desiccated coconut

1. Drain almonds and process in a food processor until they resemble fine crumbs.
2. Add the bananas, cacao, coconut oil, and lemon juice and process until the mixture is a smooth paste.
3. Add 1½ cups of the coconut, and process again.
4. Roll the mixture into balls, and coat the balls in the remaining coconut (they will be soft and will firm up when chilled).
5. Place in the refrigerator for 4 hours or overnight.

Most people think that ageing is irreversible. We know that there are mechanisms even in the human machinery that allow for the reversal of ageing, through correction of diet, through antioxidants, through removal of toxins from the body, through exercise, through yoga and breathing techniques, and through meditation.

DEEPAK CHOPRA

CHIA PUDDING

Preparation time: 10 minutes

Serves: 6 to 8

We are pre-programmed to look for sweet foods because they supply instant energy and fuel. Our ancestors were fortunate that sweet foods were not readily available so their intake of sweets was limited. Sweets were limited to berries, fruits, and the occasional wild honeycomb. Today, sugar and other dangerous sweeteners are present in just about every commercial food. Children and adults now crave sugar, and expect it every day. I remember my nutritionist saying that birthday cakes had now become everyday-cakes. The number-one cause of premature ageing today is sugar and other high-glycemic empty foods that convert to sugar when eaten.

400 ml can coconut cream (find a brand with no additives)

150 ml cream

.08 g stevia (2 scoops of Nirvana or 6 drops of liquid stevia)

¼ cup white chia seeds

1 cup strawberries, sliced

1 cup any other type of fruit, chopped

1. Combine coconut cream, stevia, and cream in a mixing bowl.
2. Add the chia seeds, then place in the fridge for an hour to thicken.
3. Stir well to make sure the chia seeds are evenly distributed in the pudding.
4. Add the fruit and mix, then spoon into individual dishes.
5. Cover with plastic and place in the fridge again to fully set (approximately 3 hours).

STEWED APPLE WITH STRAWBERRIES

Preparation time: 10 minutes

Serves: 4

4 red apples, sliced

1 cup frozen strawberries, sliced

¾ cup filtered water

1 tsp arrowroot or kuzu, mixed with 2 tsp water

Cinnamon (optional)

.04 g stevia (1 scoop of Nirvana or 3 drops of liquid stevia)

1. Place water, stevia, and apple in a saucepan and sprinkle with cinnamon.

2. Cover and simmer for approximately 10 minutes (or until apple is soft).

3. Remove apple with a slotted spoon, add arrowroot or kuzu to the remaining liquid and whisk until thick.

4. Pour sauce over the apples, add berries and stir.

5. Serve on its own or with custard.

Pouring custard

Preparation time: 15 minutes

Serves: 4 to 6

300 ml organic pure cream

½ cup water

Vanilla bean or 1 tsp of vanilla extract (page 166)

6 egg yolks

1 tbsp raw honey

1 tsp arrowroot or kuzu, mixed with 2 tsp water (optional)

1. Place egg yolks in a bowl and stir with a whisk.

2. Heat cream, water, and vanilla, while stirring, until it reaches 80 °C.

3. Add a small amount of the cream mixture to the eggs, and whisk thoroughly. Slowly add the remainder while whisking.

4. Return to the saucepan, cook on low heat, stirring continuously with a whisk, until it reaches 78°C. The mixture will start thickening around 70°C, and will get much thicker once it reaches the 78°C. For a thicker custard, add arrowroot or kuzu once the mixture reaches 70°C.

5. Remove from the heat (don't allow it to get hotter than 78°C, or it may curdle).

6. Allow to cool to 50°C, add the honey and mix thoroughly.

7. Pour into a small jug to serve.

BAKED CUSTARD

Preparation time: 10 minutes

Baking time: 30 minutes

Serves: 4 to 6

Stevia is a herb and is about 1000 times sweeter than sugar. Additionally, stevia is known to assist in balancing blood sugar levels, making it ideal for anyone coming off of caffeinated beverages or weaning themselves from sweets.

PAUL CHEK, HOW TO EAT, MOVE AND BE HEALTHY!

600 ml thin, pure cream

3 eggs

1 tbsp vanilla extract

⅛ tsp stevia

Nutmeg, ground or freshly grated

1. Preheat oven to 120°C (140°C if oven is not fan forced).
2. Mix all the ingredients together with a whisk (don't beat it, but stir well).
3. Place some water in a large baking dish (approximately half full).
4. Pour mixture into ramekins, sprinkle with nutmeg, and place ramekins into the water bath.
5. Bake for approximately 30 minutes, until the custard puffs slightly. If they aren't puffing, turn the heat up.
6. Cool them in the refrigerator until set (1 to 2 hours).

TIP: For a tasty variation, place stewed apple at the bottom of each ramekin.

APPLE CRUMBLE

Preparation time: 15 minutes

Baking time: 15 minutes

Serves: 4 to 6

Apples are very high in fructose, but they prevent blood glucose levels from rising as much as they would otherwise because they are high in fibre, and contain a phytonutrient called phloretin, which has been proven to stabilise blood sugar levels. This nutritious substance is only found in apples. Apples are also very high in antioxidants, because of their strong red and green colours.

¾ cup almond meal

½ cup coconut flour

1 cup desiccated coconut

150 g butter

6 apples

¼ cup sultanas or cranberries

¾ cup filtered water

1 tsp arrowroot or kuzu, mixed with 2 tsp water

1. Preheat oven to 130°C (150°C if oven is not fan forced).

2. Place the filtered water and the sultanas in a saucepan, and heat gently.

3. Slice the apple, and place in the saucepan.

4. Cover and simmer until the apple is soft (approximately 10 minutes).

5. Remove apple with a slotted spoon, add arrowroot or kuzu to the remaining liquid and whisk until thick.

6. Pour sauce over apples and mix.

7. Place dry ingredients and butter in the food processor and process.

8. The crumble can be served traditionally or deconstructed.

9. If deconstructing, place the crumble in a baking dish, and bake for approximately 15 minutes or until golden (toss half way through).

10. For a traditional crumble, place the apple mixture in a baking dish, cover with crumble, and bake for 15 minutes.

CHOCOLATE MOUSSE

Preparation time: 25 minutes

Serves: 6 to 8

60 g cacao butter

3 tbsp raw cacao powder

4 sheets gelatine (titanium strength)

4 tbsp filtered water

3 eggs, separated

1½ tsp vanilla extract (page 166)

2½ tbsp raw honey

200 ml organic, pure cream

1. Soak the gelatine in cold filtered water.

2. In a saucepan, on a very gentle heat, melt the cacao butter, and add the cacao, vanilla, and filtered water.

3. Squeeze the excess water from the gelatine.

4. Remove the chocolate mixture from the heat, add the softened gelatine and whisk until completely dissolved.

5. Add the egg yolks, and whisk until thickened and smooth.

6. Set aside to cool.

7. Whip the cream, and set aside.

8. In a separate bowl, beat the egg whites until stiff peaks form.

9. Slowly add the honey while beating, and continue until the mixture is glossy.

10. Stir the cream to make sure it hasn't fallen any (if it has, fluff it up with a whisk).

11. Whisk the chocolate mixture for a few seconds to remove the skin, and gently fold it into the cream.

12. Beat the egg whites again for a second to make sure they haven't fallen, and gently fold the chocolate mixture into the egg whites.

13. Pour into glasses to chill (2 to 3 hours) and serve with whipped cream.

Downey considered that gelatine was recognised as a valuable addition to the diet because of its easy digestion, ready absorption, protein-sparing ability and supplementary protein value. He also noted that gelatine aided in the digestion of other foods, especially milk and milk products, and served as a base for many attractive and appealing dishes.

N.R. GOTTHOFFER, GELATIN IN NUTRITION AND MEDICINE

ICE CREAM

The following ice cream recipes are very easy to make; they don't require an ice cream maker, and they only take approximately 10 minutes to prepare.

If you put the container of frozen ice cream in the fridge ½ hour before serving, it is easier to scoop. You can also put the ice cream into individual containers, which means you can pull a single-serving out of the freezer.

In the old days when ice cream was made of whole eggs, cream and sugar and laboriously cranked out in the old home freezer, a serving of ice cream was only an occasional family treat that didn't do much harm. Today in this mass producing, synthetic age, it is another matter entirely. Today you may be treating your family to poison! Ice cream manufacturers are not required by law to list the additives used in the manufacturing of their product. Consequently, today most ice creams are synthetic from start to finish.

Analysis has shown the following:

DIETHYLGLYCOL: A cheap chemical used as an emulsifier instead of eggs is the same chemical used in antifreeze and paint removers.

PIPERNAL: Used in place of vanilla. This chemical is used to kill lice.

ALDEHYDE C-17: Used to flavour cherry ice cream. It is an inflammable liquid also used in aniline dyes, plastic, and rubber.

ETHYL ACETATE: Used to give ice cream a pineapple flavour—and as a cleaner for leather and textiles; its vapours have been known to cause chronic lung, liver, and heart damage.

BUTYRALDEHYDE: Used in nut flavoured ice cream. It is one of the ingredients of rubber cement.

AMYLACETATE: Used for its banana flavour. It is also used as an oil paint solvent.

BENZYL ACETATE: Used for its strawberry flavour. It is a nitrate solvent.

The next time you are tempted by a luscious looking banana split sundae made with commercial ice cream, think of it as a mixture of antifreeze, oil paint, nitrate solvent, and lice killer, and you won't find it so appetizing.
—*PPNF Health Journal*

ICE CREAM

Preparation time: 10 minutes
Serves: 8

Vanilla

600 ml organic pure cream
8 egg yolks
1½ tbsp raw honey
Vanilla bean

1. Whip cream with an electric beater until almost completely whipped (not yet forming stiff peaks, but almost to that point).

2. Add yolks, one at a time, while continually whipping. Whip until fluffy.

3. Add seeds from the vanilla bean.

4. Add honey slowly while whipping.

5. Pour into an airtight container and freeze.

Chocolate

600 ml organic pure cream
2 tbsp quality cocoa
8 egg yolks
2½ tbsp raw honey
Vanilla bean

1. Pour cream into a large mixing bowl and add the cocoa.

2. Whip cream with an electric beater until almost completely whipped (not yet forming stiff peaks, but almost to that point). The cocoa will slowly dissolve while whipping.

3. Add yolks, one at a time, while continually whipping. Whip until fluffy.

4. Add seeds from the vanilla bean.

5. Add honey slowly while whipping.

6. Pour into an airtight container and freeze.

Strawberry

600 ml organic pure cream
8 egg yolks
Vanilla bean
450 g ripe strawberries
1½ tbsp raw honey

1. Purée the strawberries and honey in a food processor, and set aside.

2. Whip cream with an electric beater until almost completely whipped (not yet forming stiff peaks, but almost to that point).

3. Add yolks, one at a time, while continually whipping. Whip until fluffy.

4. Add seeds from the vanilla bean.

5. Slowly add the strawberry mixture, and whip until as fluffy as possible. The strawberries weigh the mixture down, so it may not be as fluffy as the vanilla or chocolate ice cream (depending on the brand of cream).

6. Pour into an airtight container and freeze.

ICE CREAM CAKE

Preparation time: 30 minutes

Serves: 16

Ingredients for a half recipe of two flavours of ice cream (page 188)

100 ml organic cream or melted chocolate (page 168)

1. Prepare the ice cream for the bottom layer.

2. Pour the ice cream mixture into a spring form cake pan, and place into the freezer for a few hours.

3. Prepare the second flavour (for the top of the cake). Remove the cake tin from the freezer, and pour the second flavour on top of the bottom layer.

4. Cover with plastic, return to the freezer, and freeze all day or overnight.

5. An hour before icing the cake, place a platter in the freezer to keep the cake from melting.

6. Remove the cake from the freezer, wipe the outside of the tin with a wet cloth, release the spring, and remove the outside of the tin.

7. Use a spatula to separate the cake from the bottom of the pan, slide the cake onto the platter, and remove the bottom of the tin.

8. Return the cake to the freezer while the icing is prepared.

9. The cake can be decorated with whipped cream or melted chocolate. If the chocolate has just been made, it can simply be poured on the cake. If melting chocolate, follow steps 2 to 7 on page 168 to temper the chocolate.

10. Use a large straight-edged knife to cut.

Sugar is a type of bodily fuel, yes, but your body runs about as well on it as a car would.

V.L. ALLINEARE

STRAWBERRY AND BANANA CREAM ICE BLOCKS

Preparation time: 20 minutes

Serves: 10 ice blocks

[The Rosicky family were known] not to hurry through life, not to be skimping and saving. They saw their neighbours buy more land and feed more stock than they did, without discontent. Once when the creamery agent came to the Rosickys to persuade them to sell him their cream, he told them how much the Fasslers, their nearest neighbours, had made on their cream last year. "Yes," said Mary, "And look at them Fassler children! Pale, pinched little things, they look like skimmed milk. I'd rather put some colour into my children's faces than put money into the bank."

WILLA CATHER, NEIGHBOUR ROSICKY

Strawberry

350g frozen strawberries

½ cup water

.16 g stevia (4 scoops of Nirvana or 12 drops of liquid stevia)

1 tsp raw honey

1. Place all ingredients in a food processor and process until smooth. Add a little more water if necessary.

2. Pipe or spoon into an ice block mould and place in the freezer to set a little while the banana is prepared.

Banana cream

2 large bananas

½ lemon, juiced

200 ml cream

.12 g stevia (3 scoops of Nirvana or 9 drops of liquid stevia)

3 egg yolks

1. Process bananas, stevia and lemon in a food processor until smooth.

2. Whip the cream until almost fully whipped.

3. Add the egg yolks one at a time while continuously whipping.

4. Whip until as fluffy as possible.

5. Fold through the banana mixture.

6. Pipe or spoon the mixture on top of the strawberry flavour and freeze all day or overnight. To release the ice blocks, simply run the outside of the mould under warm water for a few seconds and then pull the ice block from the mould.

CREAMY CHOC-COATED ICE BLOCKS

This recipe does take a little time to prepare, but there is nothing more rewarding than the crunch of a choc-dipped ice cream you made yourself. And, this is a great hands on activity to do with children if you have any in your household.

You can make a half recipe, but they disappear so quickly, it is well worth making a large batch.

Preparation time: 50 minutes

Makes: 20 ice blocks

Ice cream (page 188)

Chocolate (page 168)

2 ice block moulds

1. Choose two flavours of ice cream (page 188).

2. Make the 2 batches of ice cream.

3. Pipe or spoon the mixture into the moulds (piping is easier), 1 flavour on the bottom, 1 on the top.

4. Place into the freezer overnight.

5. Place a large plate or tray into the freezer as well (for later use when dipping the ice blocks).

6. Make the chocolate (page 168).

7. Pour the chocolate into a deep mug or something of similar shape (so the ice blocks can be fully dipped).

8. Remove the ice blocks from the mould by holding the mould under lukewarm water for a few seconds, then gently pulling on the stick.

9. Dip each ice block into the chocolate, remove, then hold over the mug until it stops dripping.

10. If you are working alone, hold one ice block in one hand to set while dipping another in the other hand. This is where extra sets of hands do come in handy.

11. Once the chocolate is set a little, place onto the frozen plate (the cold plate will keep the chocolate from sticking to the plate).

12. Once all ice blocks are choc-dipped, place the plate or tray back in the freezer for an hour or 2, then transfer to an air tight container and place back in the freezer.

FRUIT ICE BLOCKS

Preparation time: 15 minutes

Makes: 10 ice blocks

4 passion fruits

2 nectarines, sliced

330 ml coconut water

.08 g stevia (2 scoops Nirvana or 6 drops liquid stevia)

1. Scoop the pulp out of the passion fruit and place in a bowl.

2. Add the coconut water and stevia and mix well.

3. Pour the liquid into ice block moulds (until ¾ full).

4. Place a few nectarine slices in each mould so they are visible from the outside.

5. Freeze overnight.

NOTE: These tasty, refreshing treats seem like they would be very high in natural sugar/ fructose, but each ice block only contains around 3 g of fructose, which is quite low. I recommend staying below 15 g of fructose per day.

Sugar may be worse for kids than it is for adults because kids react so strongly and with much wilder swings of body chemistry. Some of their body systems are not fully developed. The immune system is still developing the acquired immunity to fight off infections, and the digestive system must learn to handle the variety of foods in our diet. A child's body is learning and working continually, and sugar just causes it to work harder. These body chemistry changes not only cause physical ailments, such as allergies and asthma, but have also in many studies put children on a roller coaster of emotional effects that included hyperactivity, aggressiveness, sadness, low self-esteem, mania, sleepiness, and many more.

NANCY APPLETON, PHD, SUICIDE BY SUGAR

PINEAPPLE SORBET

Preparation time: 10 minutes

Serves: 4 to 6

2 bananas, peeled and frozen

1 pineapple, sliced and frozen

1. If you have a multipurpose juicer, add the homogenising cone and nozzle, run the fruit through the machine, and mix together.
2. Otherwise, place the fruit in a food processor and run it for around 30 seconds.
3. The fruit will still be in chunks, so will have to be left to melt a little. Every 30 seconds or minute, try to process again.
4. Eventually, it will melt enough that it will become smooth.
5. Place in the freezer in an airtight container.

TIP: Any fruit can be used. Berries are a great option.

If women are truly to enjoy food, it must become one of life's freely experienced sensuous pleasures. By eating well, women take care of themselves on the most basic level.

DR KAREN JOHNSON, TRUSTING OURSELVES: THE SOURCEBOOK OF PSYCHOLOGY FOR WOMEN

It is difficult to think of a popular beverage that is healthy—most beverages, including fruit juice—contain large amounts of concentrated sugars and other additives.

We offer the theory that the craving for both alcohol and soft drinks stems from an ancient collective memory of the kind of lacto-fermented beverages still found in traditional societies. These beverages give a lift to the tired body by supplying mineral ions depleted through perspiration and contribute to easy and thorough assimilation of food by supplying lactobacilli, lactic-acid, and enzymes.

—Sally Fallon, Nourishing Traditions

DRINKS

LIME SODA

Preparation time: 5 minutes

This drink is very flavoursome, so it is a great substitute for flavoured soda or other sugary drinks. It is also very refreshing.

Sparkling mineral water

Lime, juiced (½ per person)

Lime, cut into slices (½ per person)

.04 g stevia per person (1 scoop of Nirvana or 3 drops of liquid stevia)

Ice

1. For each glass, add the juice and stevia, fill with mineral water, and then add ice.

2. Add a few slices of lime to the drink and serve.

TIP: When I go out, I order mineral water with fresh lime; it also tastes great with tequila. Just make sure the bartender doesn't use lime cordial.

Lemon and lime juice have long been used to treat scurvy; lemon juice is also an effective diuretic. In tests of plant extracts, lemon extract was found to be effective in killing roundworms. The high acidity of lemon juice, and its disinfectant and antimicrobial properties, make it ideal for marinating raw fish. The Romans believed that lemon was an antidote for all poisons, including venomous snake bites.

SALLY FALLON, NOURISHING TRADITIONS

PINE LIME PUNCH

Preparation time: 10 minutes

Servings: 8 to 10

It's almost as if the devil sat down and listed all the criteria of a substance man could use to destroy himself. It would have to be pleasing to the eye and taste. It would have to be pure white and easily available. It would have to appeal to all the people of this world. The destroying effects would have to be subtle and take such a long time that very few would realise what was happening until it was too late. The cruellest criteria of all is it would have to be supported and distributed by the kindest, most well-meaning people. So far the devil is winning. Did you ever go to a church bake sale conducted in a grade school?

BRUCE PACETTI, DDS, PPNF HEALTH JOURNAL

1 pineapple, peeled and cut into chunks

2 litres sparkling mineral water, chilled

Juice of 4 limes

$1/8$ tsp stevia

Ice

1. Pureé the pineapple and lime juice in a food processor. Combine juice, stevia, and mineral water in a large punch bowl.

2. Add a few handfuls of ice.

3. Serve with a ladle so people can help themselves, and watch how quickly it disappears.

This punch is always a big hit with both children and adults when I have a social gathering.

BERRY SMOOTHIE

Preparation time: 5 minutes

Serves: 4

Even at the "healthiest" juice bars, a fruit smoothie contains unhealthy ingredients, such as juice made from concentrate, homogenised milk, flavoured yoghurts that contain sugar, and commercial honey (honey that has been super heated and no longer has nutritional value). You can make your own healthy version in 5 minutes.

1 banana, frozen (peel and freeze the night before)

350 g frozen mixed berries

½ cup milk

1 tsp raw honey

1½ cups yoghurt (quality brand from health food store

1. Place the yoghurt and milk into a food processor with the remaining ingredients on top.
2. Process until smooth.

NOTE: To make a pure berry smoothie, without the banana, add .16 g stevia (4 scoops Nirvana).

ICED CHOCOLATE

Preparation time: 5 minutes

Serves: 1

[Raw cacao] is jam packed with antioxidants, magnesium, and bliss nutrients that can help keep you energized, healthy and happy. This cacao is made by cold pressing the raw cacao nibs to preserve the full vitality of the raw cacao. [Raw cacao] contains up to 4 times the amount of antioxidants of traditional cacao powder.

LOVING EARTH

1½ cups milk

1 tsp raw cacao powder

.06 g stevia (1½ scoops Nirvana or 5 drops of liquid stevia)

⅛ tsp vanilla extract (page 166) or just use vanilla flavoured stevia

50 g cream, whipped (optional)

2 tsp warm filtered water

1. Place the cacao powder and stevia in a glass.
2. Add the water and combine well.
3. Pour in the milk, stir, and it's done.
4. Serve with whipped cream if desired. For the powdered chocolate effect on the cream, mix a tiny pinch of powdered stevia with cacao powder, then dust on top using a sieve.

NOTE: This is an every-day favourite in our house. Our kids love the fact that they can come home and make themselves a filling treat. They generally make it without the cream, but they do enjoy it with the whipped cream occasionally, and even with a scoop of ice cream if it is readily available.

SPORTS DRINK

Preparation time: 5 minutes

Serves: 1

1 tsp apple cider vinegar

Just under ⅛ tsp Himalayan salt

Juice of half a lime

.04 g stevia (1 scoop of Nirvana or 3 drops of liquid stevia)

Mineral water

1. Pour the vinegar, salt, lime juice, and stevia into a glass.
2. Fill the rest of the glass with mineral water.

Regardless of which sweetener is listed first, [sports and vitamin drinks] all unbalance your body chemistry. My position is that supplemental vitamins and minerals are useless when taken with sugar.

NANCY APPLETON, PHD, SUICIDE BY SUGAR

Sports drinks are designed to help rehydrate and restore electrolytes and carbohydrates during or after exercise. Replacing electrolytes helps hydrate the body, which helps prevent fatigue. However, the commercial sports drinks available are a cocktail of sugar and chemicals. Here is the list of ingredients for a common brand: water, sucrose, maltodextrin, food acids (330, 331), flavour, tri-potassium citrate, sodium chloride, tri-potassium phosphate, colour (133). You can make your own healthy version that tastes great.

HOT CHOCOLATE

Preparation time: 5 minutes

Serves: 2

3 cups whole milk

2 tsp raw cacao powder

.12 g stevia (3 scoops of Nirvana or 9 drops of liquid stevia)

1. Place ingredients in a saucepan and whisk while heating gently until just hot.

2. To add the froth, whisk vigourously, or use a hand-held frother.

NOTE: You can add a dollop of whipped cream on top.

As a small boy I used to spend my school vacation on a farm where the animals received no food except that which they could find in the pasture and woods. These were not heavy milk producers with enormous udders. The cows were never ill; the need for a veterinarian was negligible. Contrast this with championship milkers with their large udders which are usually afflicted with mastitis and its associated discharge of pus. This unsavoury condition usually requires almost continuous use of penicillin to keep the milk flowing. These champions are fed objectionable concentrates of other materials at odds with Enzyme Nutrition. What will you have; less good milk or an abundance of milk incriminated as a cause of heart and artery disease?

EDWARD HOWELL, MD, ENZYME NUTRITION

CHAI LATTE

Preparation time: 10 minutes

Serves: 2

Dr V G Heiser in a recent talk to the National Association of Manufacturers told of experiments on 4,000 rats in which half were fed on a natural diet and the other half received the kind of food the average family uses. At the end of two years, the first group was essentially free from disease while the group partaking of human diet was afflicted with a number of diseases including gout, gastric ulcer, arthritis and tuberculoses.

EDWARD HOWELL, MD, FOOD ENZYMES FORHEALTH AND LONGEVITY

3 cups filtered water

2 tea bags (black tea)

1 star anise

1 cinnamon stick

3 cardamom pods, cracked open

1½ cup whole milk

.12 g stevia (3 scoops of Nirvana or 9 drops of liquid stevia)

1. Place the tea, star anise, cinnamon, and cardamom in the water and bring to the boil.

2. Boil for around 5 minutes.

3. Gently squeeze the tea bags and remove.

4. Add the stevia and milk, stir well, and keep on the heat until the tea is hot.

5. Remove the cinnamon sticks, pods, and star anise, then whisk. Use a hand-held frother to froth the tea.

TIP: For a super quick chai latte, use the same method with a pre-prepared chai blend from the health food store or supermarket.

RECOMMENDED READING

Helpful websites

Westonaprice.org **is a non-profit organisation that educates** about Dr. Weston Price's research, which demonstrated that humans achieve perfect health only when they consume nutrient-dense whole foods and the vital fat-soluble activators found exclusively in animal fats.

wisefood.com.au **is run by Julie phillips.** Her quest for the wisdom of 'food as medicine' started in the late 80's. With an open mind for uncovering the truth, her journey passionately continues. Julie offers private consultations in Shiatsu Massage, oriental Medicine and Food as Medicine. She also runs Wise Food seminars and gives lectures at the College of oriental Medicine. Phone consultations are available interstate and internationally. Her speciality is paediatrics.

Health Freedom News is available from *thenhf.com.* It is a magazine that features articles about the latest methods of alternative healing, threats to health, vaccinations, fluoridation, mercury fillings, aspartame, environmental toxins, violations of freedom by FDA raids on doctors, nutrition centres and makers of nutrition, health products, and more.

Mercola.com provides articles about the most up to date natural health information. It also exposes corporate, government, and mass media hype that causes ill-health.

Health and nutrition books

Food Enzymes for Health and Longevity, by Edward Howell.

How to Eat, Move, and Be Healthy! by Paul Chek.

The Body Knows...How to Stay Young, by Caroline Sutherland.

The Great Cholesterol Con: The Truth about What Really Causes Heart Disease and How to Avoid It, by Malcolm Kendrick.

Fat and Cholesterol are Good For You, by Uffe Ravnskov.

Why We Get Fat...And What to Do About it, Gary Taubes

Nourishing Traditions, by Sally Fallon and Mary G. Enig.

Suicide by Sugar: A Startling Look at Our #1 National Addiction, by Nancy Appleton and G. N. Jacobs.

Sugar Blues, by William Dufty.

Grain Brain, by David Perlmutter.

Low Cholesterol Leads to an Early Death, by Dr David Evans.

Vitamin K2 and the Calcium Paradox, by Kate Rheaume-Bleue.

Eat Fat, Lose Fat, by Mary Enig and Sally Fallon.

Death by Food Pyramid, by Denise Minger.

How Statin Drugs Really Lower Cholesterol: And Kill You One Cell at a Time by James and Hannah Yoseph

Heartburn Cured: The Low Carb Miracle, by Norm Robillard

You Can Heal Your Life, by Louise L. Hay. It you want to investigate the emotional causes of health issues.

Women, Food and God, by Geneen Roth. If you want to investigate emotional eating habits.

Acknowledgements

The author thankfully acknowledges permission to print excerpts from the following books:

Awakening to the Secret Code of Your Mind, by Darren R. Weissman. Copyright © 2010. Reprinted by permission of Hay House.

Food Enzymes for Health and Longevity, by Edward Howell. Copyright ©1994. Reprinted with permission from by Edward Howell, MD, Lotus Press, Po Box 325, Twin Lakes, WI 53181. All Rights Reserved.

How to Eat, Move, and Be Healthy! by Paul Chek. Copyright © 2004. Reprinted by permission of the C.H.E.K. Institute.

Know Your Fats, by Mary Enig. Copyright © 2001. Reprinted by permission of Sally Fallon, Weston A. Price Foundation.

Power, Freedom and Grace by Deepak Chopra. Copyright © 2006. Reprinted by permission of Amber-Allen Publishing, P. O. Box 6657, San Rafael, California. All rights reserved.

The Body Knows How to Stay Young by Caroline Sutherland. Copyright © 2008. Reprinted by permission of Hay House.

The Cholesterol Myths: Exposing the Fallacy that Saturated Fat and Cholesterol Cause Heart Disease, by Uffe Ravnskov. Copyright © 2002. Reprinted by permission of Uffe Ravnskov, New Trends Publishing.

The Great Cholesterol Con: The Truth about What Really Causes Heart Disease and How to Avoid It, by Malcolm Kendrick. Copyright © 2007. Reprinted by permission of John Blake Publishing.

The Power of Infinite Love & Gratitude, by Darren R. Weissman. Copyright © 2005. Reprinted by permission of Hay House.

The use of Gelatin in Nutrition and Medicine, by Nathan Ralph Gotthoffer. Copyright © 1945. Reprinted by permission of Grayslake Gelatin Company.

Nourishing Traditions: The Cookbook that Challenges Politically Correct Nutrition and the Diet Dictocrats, by Sally Fallon and Mary Enig. Copyright © 2001. Reprinted by permission of Sally Fallon, Weston A. Price Foundation, New Trends Publishing.

Sugar Blues, by William Dufty. Copyright © 1993. Reprinted by permission of Grand Central Publishing.

Suicide by Sugar: A Startling Look at our #1 National Addiction, by Nancy Appleton and G. N. Jacobs. Copyright © 2009. Adapted by permission of Square one Publishers.

Trusting ourselves: the Sourcebook of Psychology for Women, by Karen Johnson. Copyright © 1991. Reprinted by permission of Grove/Atlantic.

Women's Bodies, Women's Wisdom, by Christiane Northrup. Copyright © 1998. Reprinted by permission of Piatkus Books.

You Can Heal Your Life, by Louise Hay. Copyright © 2004. Reprinted by permission of Hay House.

The author thankfully acknowledges permission to print excerpts from the following articles:

Health Freedom News. Reprinted by permission of the National Health Federation.

Price-Pottenger Nutrition Foundation Health Journal. Reprinted by permission of the Price-Pottenger Nutrition Foundation Journal of Health and Healing, ppnf.org.

lovingearth.net. Reprinted by permission of Living Earth Pty Ltd (trading as Loving Earth).

westonaprice.org. Reprinted by permission of Sally Fallon, Weston A.. Price Foundation.

References

Abrams, H. Leon Jr. (1980). "Vegetarianism: An anthropological/nutritional evaluation," in Journal of Applied Nutrition 32: 53-87. *biblelife.org/abrams2.htm*, last accessed October 2010.

Abrams, H. Leon Jr. (1987). "The preference for animal protein and fat: A cross-cultural survey." A paper originally presented at the 94th Symposium of the Wenner-Gren Foundation for Anthropological Research, Cedar Key, Florida, October 23-30, 1983. In Food and Evolution: Toward a Theory of Human Food Habits, ed. Marvin Harris and Eric B. Ross. Philadelphia: Temple University Press, pp. 207-223.

Appleton, Nancy and Jacobs, G. N. (2009). Suicide by Sugar: A Startling Look at Our #1 National Addiction. Garden City Park, New York: Square One Publishers.

Berry, William (1974). "Agriculture for a Small Planet", a symposium presented in Spokane, Washington, July 1, 1974. In The Unsettling of America: Culture & Agriculture (1996). Berkeley: University of California Press.

Bieler, Henry G. (1966). Food Is Your Best Medicine: New York: Random House. Reprint, Ballantine Books (1982), pp. 99, 206.

Blesso, C (2013). "Whole egg consumption improves lipoprotein profiles and insulin sensitivity to a greater extent than yolk-free egg substitute in individuals with metabolic syndrome." Available at: *http://www.ncbi.nlm.nih.gov/pubmed/23021013*. Last accessed February 2014.

Cather, Willa (1928). "Neighbour Rosicky," first published in Obscure Destinies (1932). Reprinted in Five Stories (1956), New York: Vintage Books and in Sharon O'Brien, ed., Stories, Poems and Other Writings by Willa Cather (1984) Library of America, Viking Press, pp. 587-618. *shortstoryclassics.50megs.com/catherneighbour.html*, last accessed August 2010.

Chek, Paul (2004). How to Eat, Move, and Be Healthy! San Diego, California: C.H.E.K. Institute.

Chopra, Deepak (2006). Power, Freedom and Grace: Living from the Source of Lasting Happiness. San Rafael, California: Amber-Allen Publishing.

Cohen, Robert (2001). "Calcium in Bone Disease." Available at: *notmilk.com/deb/092098.html*, last accessed June 2010.

Davis, Eric (2003). Back to Cooking Basics. Margate Beach, Queensland (Australia): Eric Davis Dental Practice.

Douglass, William Campbell II (1984). The Milk Book: How Science Is Destroying Nature's Nearly Perfect Food. Reprinted as The Milk Book or The Milk of Human Kindness Is Not Pasteurised: How Science is Destroying Nature's Nearly Perfect Food (1995, 2003), World Trade Center, Panama City, Republic of Panama: Rhino Publishing SA, pp. 175, 211, 216.

Douglass, William Campbell II (2003). Eat Your Cholesterol: How to Live off the Fat of the Land and Feel Great. Panama City, Republic of Panama: Rhino Publishing SA.

Dreon, Detal (1998). "Change in dietary saturated fat intake is correlated with change in mass of large low-density-lipoprotein particles in men." Available at: *http://ajcn.nutrition.org/content/67/5/828.short*. Last accessed February 2014.

Dufty, William (1993). Sugar Blues, rev. 2nd ed. New York: Grand Central Publishing.

Enig, Mary G. (2009). "Know Your Fats." Available at: *westonaprice.org/know-your-fats.html*, last accessed October 2010.

Enig, Mary G. (2006). "The Latest Studies on Coconut Oil." Available at: *westonaprice.org/know-your-fats/534-latest-studies-on-coconut-oil.html*, last accessed August 2010.

Enig, Mary G. and Fallon, Sally A. (1999). "Modern-day diets high in hydrogenated vegetable oils instead of traditional animal fats are implicated in causing a significant increase in heart disease and cancer", in Nexus Magazine 6(2). Extract: *oralchelation.net/heartdisease/ChapterFive/page5c.htm*, last accessed June 2010.

Evans, D. (2012). Cholesterol and Saturated Fat Prevent Heart Disease—Evidence from 101 Scientific Papers. Guilford, Surrey: Grosvenor House Publishing Ltd.

Evans, D. (2012). Low Cholesterol Leads to an Early Death—Evidence from 101 Scientific Papers. Guilford, Surrey: Grosvenor House Publishing Ltd.

Fallon, Sally (1995). "Vitamin A Vagary," in PPNF Health Journal, Price-Pottenger Nutrition Foundation, 19(2): 1-3. realmilk.com/vita.html Revised as "Vitamin A Saga". *westonaprice.org/abcs-of-nutrition/167-vitamin-a-saga.html*, last accessed June 2013.

Fallon, Sally and Enig, Mary G. (1999, 2001). Nourishing Traditions: The Cookbook that Challenges Politically Correct Nutrition and the Diet Dictocrats, Rev. 2nd ed. Washington DC: New Trends Publishing.

Fallon, Sally and Enig, Mary G. (2003). "Diet and Disease: Not What You Think." Available at: *coconut-info.com/diet_and_disease.htm*, last accessed August 2010.

Gotthoffer, Nathan Ralph (1945). Gelatin in Nutrition and Medicine. Grayslake, Illinois: Grayslake Gelatin Company. Copy held by the Library of Congress. Email: *ada@loc.gov*.

Gurr, Michael (1996). "A Fresh Look at Dietary Recommendations," in Inform 7(4): pp 432-435.

Gurr, Michael, Harwood, John L., and Frayn, Kieth N. (2002). Lipid Biochemistry: An Introduction, 5th ed. New York: Wiley-Blackwell.

Fife, Bruce (2004). The Coconut Oil Miracle. New York: The Penguin Group.

Ho, Kok-Sun et al (2012). "Stopping or reducing dietary fiber intake reduces constipation and its associated symptoms." Available at: *http://www.ncbi.nlm.nih.gov/pmc/articles/PMC3435786/*. Last accessed February 2014.

Holmberg, S et al (2013). "High dairy fat intake related to less central obesity: a male cohort study with 12 years' follow-up." Available at: *http://www.ncbi.nlm.nih.gov/pubmed/%2023320900*. Last accessed February 2014.

Howell, Edward (1985). Enzyme Nutrition: The Food Enzyme Concept. New York: Avery (Penguin Putnam Publishers), pp. 42, 43.

Howell, Edward (1994). Food Enzymes for Health and Longevity, 2nd ed. Twin Lakes, Wisconsin: Lotus Press, p. 123.

Hutchinson, Woods (1911). A Handbook of Health. New York: Houghton Mifflin Company.

Jackson, T (2013). "How science is going sour on sugar." Available at: *http://www.bmj.com/content/346/bmj.f307*. Last accessed February 2014.

Joel, Alan (2010). "How Much Water Should You Really Drink?"Available at: *"ezinearticles.com/?How-Much-Water-Should-You-Really-Drink?&id=1837549*, last accessed August 2010.

Johnson, Karen, and Ferguson, Tom (1990). Trusting Ourselves: The Sourcebook of Psychology for Women. New York: Atlantic Monthly Press.

Kendrick, Malcolm (2007). The Great Cholesterol Con: The Truth about What Really Causes Heart Disease and How to Avoid It. London: John Blake Publishing.

Krauss, R et al (2010). "Meta-analysis of prospective cohort studies evaluating the association of saturated fat with cardiovascular disease." Available at: *http://ajcn.nutrition.org/content/early/2010/01/13/ajcn.2009.27725.abstract*. Last accessed February 2014.

Lawrence, G (2013). "Dietary fats and health: dietary recommendations in the context of scientific evidence." Available at: *http://www.ncbi.nlm.nih.gov/pubmed/23674795*. Last accessed February 2014.

Lee, William H (1982). The Friendly Bacteria. New Canaan, Connecticut: Keats Publishing. Reprinted as William C. Y. Lee, The Friendly Bacteria (1999). New York: McGraw-Hill, 1999, p. 28.

Lennerz, B et al (2013). "Effects of dietary glycemic index on brain regions related to reward and craving in men." Available at: *http://ajcn.nutrition.org/content/early/2013/06/26/ajcn.113.064113.abstract*. Last accessed February 2014.

Lustig, Robert (2012). Fat Chance: The Hidden Truth about Sugar, Obesity and Disease. Toronto, Canada: Harper Collins Publishers.

MacBean, Valerie (2001). Coconut Cookery. Mumbai, India: Frog Books, p. 13.

Malhotra, A (2013). "Saturated fat is not the major issue." Available at: *http://www.bmj.com/content/347/bmj.f6340*. Last accessed February 2014.

Malhotra, A (2013). "The dietary advice on added sugar needs emergency surgery." Available at: *http://www.bmj.com/content/346/bmj.f3199*. Last accessed February 2014.

Matthews, R (2013). "Heart disease: Is sugar the real killer?" Available at: *http://www.thenational.ae/news/uae-news/technology/heart-disease-is-sugar-the-real-killer*. Last accessed February 2014.

Mente, A et al (2009). "A systematic review of the evidence supporting a causal link between dietary factors and coronary heart disease." Available at: *http://www.ncbi.nlm.nih.gov/pubmed/19364995*. Last accessed February 2014.

Mercola, Joseph (2008). "My One-Hour Vitamin D Lecture to Clear up All Your Confusion on This Vital Nutrient." *articles.mercola.com/sites/articles/archive/2008/12/16/my-one-hour-vitamin-d-lecture-to-clear-up-all-your-confusion-on-this-vital-nutrient.aspx*, last accessed September 2010.

Minger, D (2013). Death by Food Pyramid. Malibu, CA: Primal Blueprint Publishing.

Mudd, Chris (1988). Cholesterol and Your Health: The Great American Rip Off, Part I. Oklahoma City, Oklahoma: American Lite Co.

Newbold, H. L. (1991). Dr. Newbold's Type A / Type B Weight Loss Book. New Canaan, Connecticut: Keats Publishing.

Nienheiser, Jil, ed. (1999). "Myths and Truths about Nutrition. Weston Price Foundation." Available at: *westonaprice.org/abcs-of-nutrition/265-myths-a-truths-about-nutrition.html*, last accessed August 2010.

Northrup, Christiane (1998). Women's Bodies, Women's Wisdom, rev. 2nd ed. London: Piatkus Books.

Page, Melvin E., and Abrams, H. Leon (1974). Health versus Disease, revised as Page, Melvin E. and Abrams, H Leon, Jr., Your Body Is Your Best Doctor (1991), New Canaan, Connecticut: Keats Publishing. Revised as Your Body is Your Best Doctor (2001), Bloomington, Indiana: iUniverse.

Passwater, Richard A. (1978). Cancer and Its Nutritional Therapies. New Canaan, Connecticut: Keats Publishing, pp. 2-114.

Penny, S (2013). "Acid is Stored in our Fat Cells – Scientific Study." Available at: *http://symbiosis4u.us/Redox/Science/Acid%20is%20Stored%20in%20our%20Fat%20Cells.pdf*. Last accessed February 2014.

Ravnskov, Uffe (2009). Fat and Cholesterol are Good for You! Washington, D. C. and Winona Lake, Indiana: New Trends Publishing.

Rheaume-Bleue, Kate (2012). Vitamin K2 and the Calcium Paradox. Toronto, Canada: HarperCollins Publishers Ltd.

Roth, Geneen (2010). Women, Food and God: An Unexpected Path to Almost Everything. New York: Simon & Schuster.

Sinatra, S, Bowden, J (2012). The Great Cholesterol Myth. Beverly, MA: Fair Winds Press.

Stefansson, Vilhjalmur (1957). Not by Bread Alone, revised as The Fat of the Land (1960). New York: MacMillan, p. 112. Available at: *zerocarbage.com/library/FOTL.pdf*, last accessed July 2010.

Sutherland, Caroline (2008). The Body Knows How to Stay Young. Carlsbad, California: Hay House.

Valentine, Tom, Spounias, James D, Valentine, Carole (1995). In Search for Health: A Classic Anthology. Naples, Florida: Valentine Communications Corporation.

Valtin, Heinz (2002). "Drink at least eight glasses of water a day. Really? Is there scientific evidence for "8 × 8"?" Review. American Journal of Physiology —Regulatory, Integrative and Comparative Physiology 238(5): R993-R1004, last accessed September 2010.

Vignini, A, et al (2013). "Alzheimer's disease and diabetes: new insights and unifying therapies." Available at: *http://www.ncbi.nlm.nih.gov/pubmed/23363296*. Last accessed February 2014.

Yang, Q et al (2014). "Added Sugar Intake and Cardiovascular Diseases Mortality Among US Adults." Available at: *http://archinte.jamanetwork.com/article.aspx?articleid=1819573*. Last accessed February 2014.

Conversion Guide

Specific numbers for chocolate and custard recipes:

CELSIUS	FAHRENHEIT
25	80
27	80
28	82
30	86
31	88
50	122
60	140
70	158
78	172
80	176

Standard numbers for baking:

CELSIUS	FAHRENHEIT
100	210
120	250
130	270
140	285
150	300
160	325
180	350
190	375
200	400

Dry measures:

GRAMS (G)	OUNCES (OZ)
15	½
30	1
60	2
90	3
125	4
155	5
185	6
220	7

My own LCHF recipes

Recipe Name: _____

Ingredients:

_____   _____

_____   _____

_____   _____

_____   _____

_____   _____

_____   _____

Method:

_____

_____

_____

_____

_____

_____

Recipe Name: _____

Ingredients:

_____   _____

_____   _____

_____   _____

_____   _____

_____   _____

_____   _____

_____   _____

Method:

_____

_____

_____

_____

_____

_____

_____

Recipe Name: _____

Ingredients:

_____   _____

_____   _____

_____   _____

_____   _____

_____   _____

_____   _____

_____   _____

Method:

_____

_____

_____

_____

_____

_____

_____

_____

Recipe Name: _____

Ingredients:

_____ _____

_____ _____

_____ _____

_____ _____

_____ _____

_____ _____

_____ _____

Method:

_____

_____

_____

_____

_____

_____

_____

Recipe Name: _____

Ingredients:

_____   _____

_____   _____

_____   _____

_____   _____

_____   _____

_____   _____

_____   _____

Method:

_____

_____

_____

_____

_____

_____

_____

_____

Recipe Name: _____

Ingredients:

_____ _____

_____ _____

_____ _____

_____ _____

_____ _____

_____ _____

_____ _____

Method:

_____

_____

_____

_____

_____

_____

_____

_____

Subject Index

additives, 14

agave syrup, 16

ageing
preventing and reversing, 25, 46, 58, 148

aluminium, 15

ancestral diet, 2, 18, 176

anxiety
cures for, 26

apple-cider vinegar, 17, 18, 23

apples, 21, 176, 164, 182

arrowroot, 114

asthma, 23, 26, 196

babies and children
nutrition, 2–9, 12, 19, 22–28, 36, 54, 58, 62, 136, 176, 186, 192, 196

bacon, 80, 142

baking powder, 15

beverages
healthy, 180, 200

blood sugar, 5, 16, 18, 40, 180, 182

bone broth, 23

breakfast, 11, 18, 40

breathing, 26, 174

broth, 23

buckwheat, 7, 68, 160

butter, 2–8, 12–14, 16, 18–19, 40, 74, 78, 136, 142

calcium, 3, 11–12, 19, 114, 172

candida, 23, 86, 172

carbohydrates, 2–4, 7, 9, 10–13, 21, 24, 116, 130, 164

chemicals
in food and water 15–16, 22–23, 29, 36, 166, 186

chewing, 17

children and babies
nutrition, 2–9, 12, 19, 22–28, 36, 54, 58, 62, 136, 176, 186, 192, 196

cholecystokinin, 4

cholesterol, 2–7, 12, 16, 42, 48, 50, 58, 64, 96, 98, 122, 124, 130, 134, 170

cacao
raw, 29, 208

mass, 29, 168

butter, 29, 168

coconut oil, 2, 7, 16, 19, 24, 170, 172

colonic irrigation, 24

condiments, 88

constipation, 24–25, 38

cream, 2, 12, 13, 16, 21, 35, 78, 136, 164, 186, 192

crooked teeth
causes of, 5, 26

cultured food, 18, 24

dairy, 14, 16

desserts, 21, 22

diabetes, 1, 3, 20, 148

diets, 1–12, 23, 38, 46

digestion, 3, 5, 13–14, 18, 23, 38, 184

drinking with meals, 18

eating
emotional, 28

eggs, 2, 6–8, 12–13, 17–19, 40, 42, 44
brain food, 44

elimination, 24
squatting, 25

For further information, please visit:
christinecronau.com

To receive daily tips and connect with the LCHF community, please visit:
facebook.com/ChristineCronau